COMPLIMENTS OF
ROB AND BESSIE WELDER WILDLIFE FOUNDATION
P. O. BOX 1396
SINTON, TEXAS 78387

GRASSES OF THE TEXAS COASTAL BEND

(Upper) Fine textured upland site on the Welder Wildlife Refuge about four months after being subjected to brush control measures. The dominant grass is *Setaria leucopila*. Other major grasses are *Aristida roemeriana*, *Panicum filipes*, *Andropogon saccharoides* var. *longipaniculata*, *Tridens congestus*, *Panicum obtusum* and *Buchloe dactyloides*.

(Lower) Sandy loam site on the Welder Wildlife Refuge. The major grasses are *Andropogon gerardi*, *Panicum virgatum*, *Elyonurus tripsacoides* and *Andropogon littoralis*. In the background oak woods *Setaria scheelei* is a dominant grass. Minor grasses present are *Brachiaria ciliatissima*, *Panicum capillarioides*, *Leptoloma cognatum* and *Cenchrus incertus*.

GRASSES OF THE TEXAS COASTAL BEND

(Calhoun, Refugio, Aransas, San Patricio and northern Kleberg Counties)

Frank W. Gould
Department of Range & Forestry
Texas A&M University
   and

Thadis W. Box
Department of Agronomy and Range Management
Texas Technological College

1965

Texas A&M University Press
College Station, Texas

Welder Wildlife Foundation
contribution 34 Series C (Revised)

Published with the cooperation of the
Texas Agricultural Experiment Station

Distributed by
THE EXCHANGE STORE
TEXAS A&M UNIVERSITY
COLLEGE STATION, TEXAS
Price $3.25

PREFACE TO REVISION

This book is an expanded revision of the mimeographed treatment bearing the same title (Gould and Box, 1959). Additional records and data have been obtained from field studies and recent publications, perhaps the most significant of which are "Flowering plant and ferns of the Texas Coastal Bend counties" (Jones, Rowell and Johnston, 1961) and "Texas plants, a checklist and ecology summary" (Gould, 1962).

The writers are indebted to the Botany Department of the University of Arizona for the loan of a number of the line-drawing sketches by Mrs. Lucretia Breazeale Hamilton. Most of the fine illustrations are the product of Mrs. Valloo Z. Kapadia who worked on the drawings in the Tracy Herbarium of Texas A&M University while her husband, Zarir J. Kapadia, completed the requirements for the Ph.D. degree in the Department of Range and Forestry. The work of Mrs. Kapadia was supported by a grant from the Rob and Bessie Welder Wildlife Foundation. The excellent grass illustrations are in themselves a valuable contribution to the botany of Texas.

This publication was made possible through the support and cooperation of the Rob and Bessie Welder Wildlife Foundation and the Texas Agricultural Experiment Station. The treatment has been oriented for use in the research program of the Welder Foundation and species known to occur on the Welder Wildlife Refuge are indicated by an asterisk. Data were obtained from field observations, from the examination of plant collections in the herbaria of the Welder Foundation and the Tracy Herbarium of Texas A&M University, and from the personal collections of Dr. Clarence Cottam, W. C. Glazener, Chester M. Rowell, Jr., Fred Jones and George Williges. The plant checklists of the Welder Wildlife Refuge (Rowell 1957; Jones, Rowell and Johnston, 1961) and the checklists of Texas Grasses (Gould, 1957 and 1962) provided a basis for the listing of species. Thanks are due Dr. Marshall C. Johnston for his critical review of the manuscript and numerous suggestions for its improvement.

Work by the senior author has been conducted under the TAES research project S-1511, titled "Taxonomic Studies of Texas Grasses." The cost of printing and distribution were borne by the Welder Foundation.

CONTENTS

Introduction	1
Phylogenetic Grass Classification	3
List of Illustrations	4
Key to the Genera	8
Genera and Species	13
Glossary	183
Literature Cited	185
Index to Common Names	186

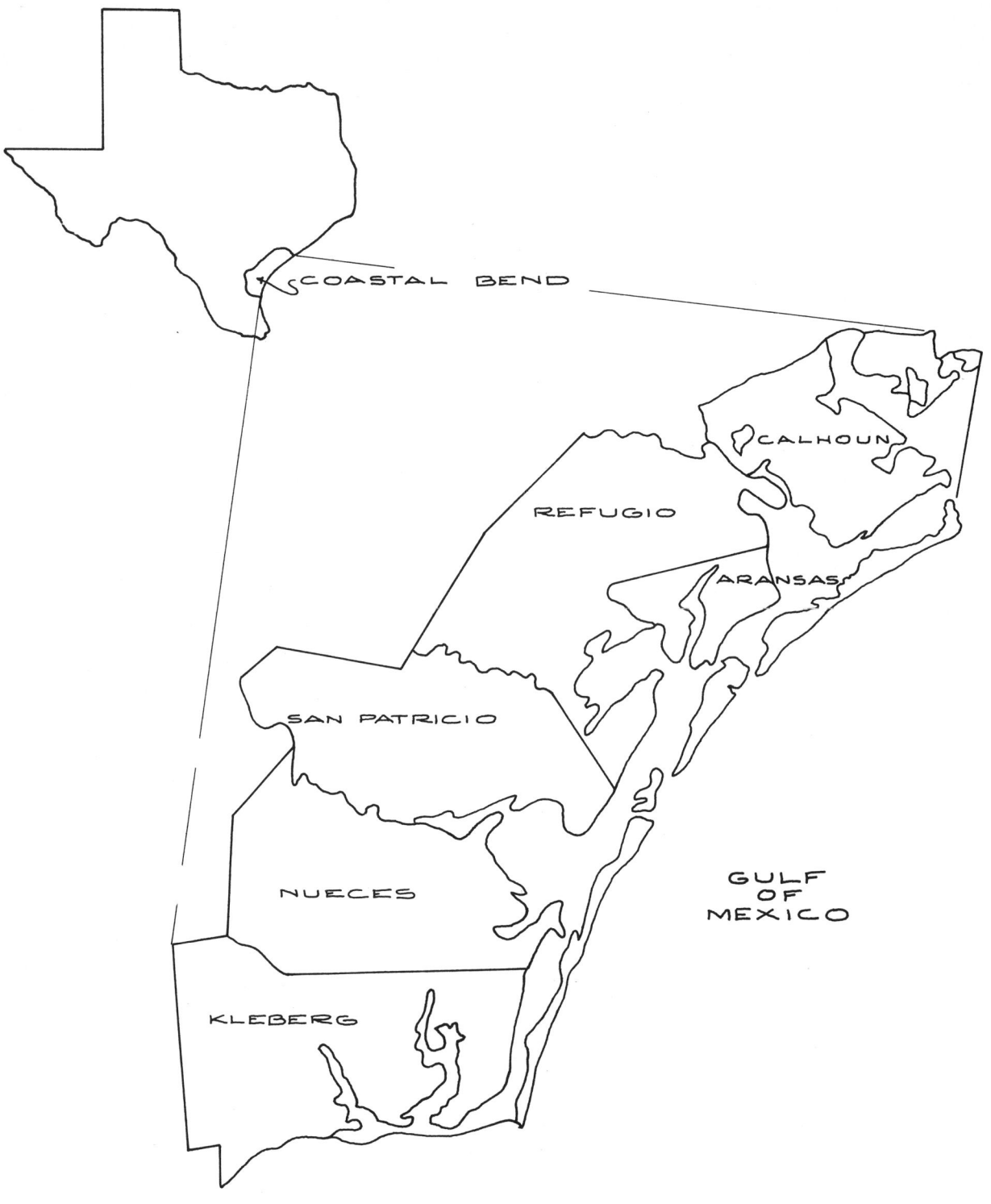

Fig. 1. Map of the Texas Coastal Bend region.

INTRODUCTION

This is a treatment of the grasses of the Coastal Bend region of Texas. The term Coastal Bend generally is used to describe the trade territory around the city of Corpus Christi, Texas. As here interpreted, it encompasses Calhoun, Refugio, Aransas, San Patricio, Nueces and the northeastern half of Kleberg counties (Figure 1). Vegetatively, the area comprises the southernmost part of the Gulf Prairie and the closely associated strip of Gulf Coast Marsh lands. Bordered on the north by a strip of the Post Oak Savannah and on the southwest by the South Texas Plains, the Coastal Bend has an exceedingly diverse flora and fauna. The grass family is especially well represented, with a total of 72 genera and 218 species. Three species are represented by two varieties.

CLIMATE. The climate of the Coastal Bend region is characterized by relatively warm temperatures in all seasons. The winters generally are short and mild. Long periods of high temperatures in the summer are not uncommon, with several weeks of temperatures near 100° F. to be expected. At Beeville, just north of the Coastal Bend region, the recorded temperature extremes are from a high of 108° F. to a low of 5° F. At Corpus Christi the extremes are from 105° F. to 11° F. Computed over a 40-year period, mean temperatures at Beeville range from 55.3° F. in January to 83.8° F. in July. On the average, killing frosts occur between December 2 in the fall and February 22 in the spring. The average length of the growing season at the Beeville station is 283 days (Norquest, 1941).

Temperature means at Corpus Christi, reported over 40 years, ranged from 56.9° F. in January to 82.7° F. in July. The average length of growing season is 335 days, with December 27 as the mean date of the first killing frost and January 26 the mean date of the last frost in the spring.

The average rainfall for the general area is near 30 inches, with averages for the principal towns as follows: Sinton, 30.62 inches; Woodsboro, 31.87; Corpus Christi, 25.84; and Refugio (Austwell), 33.89.

Because evaporation exceeds precipitation in the Coastal Bend, Thronthwaite (1948) classified this region as "semiarid." Bloodgood et al. (1954) reported the annual evaporation from an open pan at the Beeville station to be 59.11 inches, while rainfall average was 29.48 inches. This shows a potential loss of 27.96 inches from evaporation.

SOILS AND LAND USE. Dark, calcareous to neutral clay and clay loams are the predominant soils in the Coastal Bend area (Oakes *et al.*, 1958). The main series represented on the uplands are Victoria, Orelia, Tiocona and Monteola. The bottomlands are generally characterized by brown to dark gray calcareous clays and clay loams, mainly of the Leona and Frio series. Areas of clay and clay loam soils are used for pasture and for cotton, grain sorghums and vegetables.

Soils of grayish brown, near neutral sandy loams and clay loams are common throughout the area. They are mostly of the Miguel, Goliad, Medio, Zavala and Orelia series. The sites with these soils also are used for grazing and for limited production of cotton and grain sorghums.

Near the coast, large areas of eolian sand, mainly of the Nueces and Zavala series, are present. These deep sandy sites mainly are used for pasture, as severe wind erosion results when they are not protected by a permanent vegetation cover.

Saline soils are found along the coast and in low, poorly drained areas farther inland. Saline soils also have developed in limited areas where irrigation has been practiced with water containing high amounts of soluble salts.

SITES. Eight ecological sites are recognized in the Coastal Bend region. These sites were described by Box (1957) in a discussion of the vegetation of the Welder Wildlife Refuge. The sites are:

1) Fine-textured upland
2) Medium-textured, sandy loam, savannah
3) Deep sand
4) Medium-textured, mixed soil, upland
5) Fine-textured saline
6) Sandy saline
7) Inland ponds and swales
8) Alluvial river soils

The major portion of the area is comprised of the fine-textured upland site locally known as "black land" or "hog wallow" land. The soils of this site primarily are of the Victoria series, characterized by being extremely sticky and plastic when wet, and cracked when dry. The topography is generally level with poor drainage. Water stands on the surface for several days following heavy rains. Pastures on this site usually are characterized by moderate to heavy infestations of brush with the dominant shrub being running mesquite *(Prosopis glandulosa* Torr). Chaparral, consisting of a complex of brush, including blackbrush *(Acacia rigidula* Benth.), granjeno or spiny hackberry *(Celtis spinosa* Spreng. var. *pallida* (Torr.) M. C. Johnston), lotebush *(Ziziphus obtusifolia* (Hook.) A. Gray), prickly ash *(Zanthoxylum fagara* (L.) Sarg.), and agrito or agarito *(Berberis trifoliolata* Moric.), grows abundantly on other portions of the fine-textured upland site. Much of the site has been put into cultivation and is devoted to the production of cotton and grain sorghums.

The medium-textured, sandy loam savannah site covers local areas throughout the region. The major soil series are Medio, Miguel and Goliad. The use of the term "savannah" in the name is based on the scattered occurrence of live oaks *(Quercus virginiana* Mill.). There is usually an understory of shrubs beneath the live oaks, the major species being prickly ash, granjeno, agrito, lotebush and brazil or bluewood condalia *(Condalia hookeri* M. C. Johnston).

The deep sandy site is found near the coast and along inland watercourses. The soils are comprised of very fine sands, mainly of the Nueces and Medio series, and are from 4 to 30 feet in depth. The vegetation near the coast is characterized by a dense cover of scrub oak, but further inland the area is a true prairie.

Areas of medium-textured upland sites are comprised of mixed soils of the Orelia and Leona series. They are characterized by a heavy growth of shrubs and prickly pear *(Opuntia* spp.). Mesquite, granjeno, brazil, blackbrush and agrito are usually found growing in abundance.

The fine-textured saline areas are found near the bays and Gulf, and farther inland in regions of high salinity. These are heavy clay sites usually of the Leona series, although some Victoria and Orelia clays may be involved. They are characterized by dwarfed, halophytic plants and often contain dense stands of prickly pear.

The sandy saline areas are the fine sandy sites on or near the Gulf and its bays. They are usually considered beaches or dune sands and support small stunted plants of salt tolerant species or may be essentially devoid of vegetation.

The inland pond and swale site comprises nonsaline and slightly saline areas where drainage is poor. Water may catch and stand in the depressions for most of the year, resulting in semi-permanent inland lakes of various sizes. Aquatic plants are the characteristic vegetation of these areas.

Alluvial or terrace soils unlike any of the other series of the area are present immediately along the larger streams. These usually support dense stands of hackberry *(Celtis sp.)* trees. Mustang grape *(Vitis mustangensis* Buckl.) and underbrush of huisache *(Acacia farnesiana* (L.) Willd.), granjeno and prickly ash also are frequent.

PHYLOGENETIC GRASS CLASSIFICATION

For almost 50 years agrostologists of the United States used the grass classification of Bentham and Hooker as modified by A. S. Hitchcock. This system, in which the grasses are grouped in two subfamilies and 14 tribes, is based almost exclusively on morphological characteristics of the spikelet and inflorescence. Although quite satisfactory for purposes of identification and mechanical grouping of taxa, the "Hitchcock system" is now recognized as being far from "natural" in respect to phylogenetical relationships of many of the grass groups.

Considerable progress has been made in recent years toward the development of a "natural" grass classification system. The first evidence along this line came from such early studies as those of Duval-Jouve (1875) on grass leaf anatomy and of van Tieghem (1897) on the structure of the grass embryo. Perhaps the most important single contribution was made by Avdulov (1931), who correlated data from exhaustive cytological studies with anatomical and morphological evidence. Prat, (1936) in developing a similar system, extensively reviewed the findings and conclusions of others and added to the store of information with detailed studies of epidermal characters.

Several systems or modifications of systems have been presented within the last ten years, including those of Pilger (1954), Beetle (1955), Stebbins (1956), Stebbins and Crampton, (1961), Tateoka (1957) and Brown (1958). These systems basically are similar but vary in respect to numbers of tribes and subfamilies and the placement of several important genera.

In the 1961 publication by Stebbins and Crampton, the grass genera of the United States and Canada were grouped tentatively into 6 subfamilies and 26 tribes. Some 41 characters are listed by these authors as having value in the determination of systematic relationships. These characters are discussed under the headings of Inflorescence (including spikelets), Florets, Embryos, Seedlings and Roots, Stems, Leaf Structure and Anatomy, Epidermal Structure, Chemistry and Physiology, Chromosomes and Other Nuclear Structures, and Geographical Distribution.

Following the tentative system of Stebbins and Crampton, the grass genera of the Texas Coastal Bend may be grouped in 5 sub-families and 18 tribes as follows:

Subfamily Oryzoideae
    Tribe Oryzeae: *Leersia, Oryza*
    Tribe Zizanieae. *Zizaniopsis*

Subfamily Arundinoideae
    Tribe Arundineae. *Arundo, Phragmites, Cortaderia*
    Tribe Unioleae: *Uniola*
    Tribe Aristideae: *Aristida*

Subfamily Eragrostoideae
    Tribe Eragrosteae. *Eragrostis, Tridens, Triplasis, Erioneuron, Sporobolus, Muhlenbergia*
    Tribe Chlorideae: *Chloris, Trichloris, Bouteloua, Dactyloctenium, Leptochloa, Eleusine, Cynodon, Schedonnardus, Buchloe, Willkommia, Trichoneura, Hilaria*
    Tribe Spartineae: *Spartina*
    Tribe Aeluropideae: *Distichlis, Monanthochloe, Vaseyochloa, Neeragrostis*
    Tribe Pappophoreae: *Pappophorum*
    Tribe Zoysieae: *Tragus*

Subfamily Panicoideae
    Tribe Paniceae: *Panicum, Paspalum, Eriochloa, Echinochloa, Axonopus, Brachiaria Setaria, Cenchrus, Oplismenus, Digitaria, Leptoloma, Stenotaphrum*
    Tribe Andropogoneae: *Andropogon, Sorghum, Sorghastrum, Heteropogon, Trachypogon, Elyonurus, Manisurus, Tripsacum*

Subfamily Festucoideae
    Tribe Festuceae: *Festuca, Lolium, Bromus, Poa, Scleropoa, Vulpia,*
    Tribe Hordeae: *Hordeum, Elymus, Triticum*
    Tribe Aveneae: *Avena, Sphenopholis, Trisetum, Phalaris, Agrostis, Polypogon, Limnodea, Alopecurus*
    Tribe Stipeae: *Stipa*
    Tribe Monermeae: *Parapholis*

In the present treatment, the grasses of the Texas Coastal Bend are listed alphabetically, both in respect to genera and species. This procedure is followed partially for the convenience of ready reference and partially because of the present state of "flux" of the developing phylogenetic system.

GRASSES OF THE TEXAS COASTAL BEND

LIST OF ILLUSTRATIONS

Fig. 1.	Map of the Texas Coastal Bend region.
Fig. 2.	*Agrostis hiemalis.* Plant and spikelet.
Fig. 3.	*Andropogon annulatus.* Inflorescence and spikelet.
Fig. 4.	*Andropogon barbinodis.* Inflorescence and spikelet.
Fig. 5.	*Andropogon gerardi.* Plant, spikelet pair and spikelet.
Fig. 6.	*Andropogon glomeratus.* Inflorescence.
Fig. 7 a-b.	*Andropogon hybridus.* Inflorescence and spikelet pair.
Fig. 8.	*Andropogon intermedius.* Inflorescence.
Fig. 9 a-b.	*Andropogon ischaemum* var. *songaricus.* Inflorescence and spikelet pair.
Fig. 10.	*Andropogon saccharoides* var. *longipaniculata.* Inflorescence and spikelet pair.
Fig. 11.	*Andropogon saccharoides* var. *torreyanus.* Inflorescence and spikelet pair.
Fig. 12.	*Andropogon scoparius* var. *littoralis.* Raceme and spikelet pair.
Fig. 13.	*Andropogon scoparius* var. *frequens.* Plant and spikelet pair.
Fig. 14 a-b.	*Andropogon sericeus.* Inflorescence and spikelet pair.
Fig. 15 a-b.	*Andropogon ternarius.* Inflorescence and spikelet pair.
Fig. 16.	*Aristida desmantha.* Inflorescence and spikelet.
Fig. 17 a-b.	*Aristida intermedia.* Inflorescence and spikelet.
Fig. 18 a-b.	*Aristida longiseta.* Inflorescence and spikelet.
Fig. 19.	*Aristida oligantha.* Plant.
Fig. 20.	*Aristida purpurea.* Plant and spikelet.
Fig. 21.	*Aristida roemeriana.* Inflorescence.
Fig. 22 a-b.	*Arundo donax.* Branch of inflorescence and spikelet.
Fig. 23.	*Avena fatua* var. *sativa.* Spikelet.
Fig. 24.	*Axonopus affinis.* Plant and spikelet.
Fig. 25.	*Bouteloua curtipendula* var. *curtipendula.* Plant, glumes and spikelet with glumes removed.
Fig. 26.	*Bouteloua filiformis.* Plant.
Fig. 27.	*Bouteloua hirsuta.* Plant.
Fig. 28.	*Bouteloua rigidiseta.* Inflorescence.
Fig. 29 a-b.	*Bouteloua trifida.* Plant and spikelet with glumes and florets separated.
Fig. 30 a-b.	*Brachiaria ciliatissima.* Inflorescence and spikelet.
Fig. 31 a-b.	*Brachiaria platyphylla.* Plant and spikelet.
Fig. 32.	*Bromous texensis.* Inflorescence and spikelet.
Fig. 33.	*Bromus wildenowii.* Plant, spikelet and floret.
Fig. 34.	*Buchloe dactyloides.* Staminate plant (a), and male spikelet with glumes separated from the floret (b), and pistillate plant (c), with inflorescence (d), female spikelet (e) and spikelet cluster or "bur" (f).
Fig. 35.	*Cenchrus ciliare.* Plant, spikelet cluster (bur), spikelet.
Fig. 36.	*Cenchrus echinatus.* Flower cluster (bur).
Fig. 37 a-c.	*Cenchrus incertus.* Plant, bur, and spikelet.
Fig. 38.	*Cenchrus myosuroides.* Flower cluster (bur).
Fig. 39.	*Chloris andropogonoides.* Inflorescence and spikelet.
Fig. 40.	*Chloris chloridea.* Base of plant showing cleistogenes on rhizomes, leafy culm with inflorescence, aerial spikelet (left) and caryopsis of aerial spikelet (left center) and large caryopsis of subterrainian spikelet (center).
Fig. 41.	*Chloris ciliata.* Spikelet.
Fig. 42 a-b.	*Chloris cucullata.* Inflorescence and spikelet.
Fig. 43.	*Chloris gayana.* Plant and spikelet.
Fig. 44.	*Chloris latisquamea.* Spikelet.
Fig. 45 a-b.	*Chloris petraea.* Inflorescence and spikelet.
Fig. 46.	*Chloris polydactyla.* Inflorescence and spikelet.
Fig. 47.	*Chloris subdolichostachya.* **Spikelet.**

Fig. 48. *Chloris texensis*. Inflorescence and spikelet.
Fig. 49. *Chloris verticillata*. Plant and spikelet.
Fig. 50. *Chloris virgata*. Plant and spikelet with glumes separated.
Fig. 51. *Cynodon dactylon*. Plant, inflorescence and spikelet.
Fig. 52. *Dactyloctenium aegyptium*. Inflorescence and spikelet.
Fig. 53. *Digitaria californica*. Plant and spikelet.
Fig. 54 a-b. *Digitaria insularis*. Inflorescence and spikelet.
Fig. 55. *Digitaria patens*. Inflorescence and spikelet.
Fig. 56. *Digitaria runyoni*. Spikelet.
Fig. 57. *Digitaria sanguinalis*. Plant and 2 views of spikelet.
Fig. 58. *Digitaria texana*. Spikelet.
Fig. 59. *Distichlis spicata*. Plant with pistillate inflorescence and separate staminate inflorescence.
Fig. 60. *Echinochloa colonum*. Plant and spikelet.
Fig. 61 a-b. *Echinochloa crusgallii*. Inflorescence and spikelet.
Fig. 62. *Echinochloa walteri*. Inflorescence.
Fig. 63. *Eleusine indica*. Inflorescence and spikelet.
Fig. 64 a-b. *Elymus canadensis*. Plant and spikelet with glumes separated from the floret.
Fig. 65. *Elymus virginicus*. Inflorescence.
Fig. 66. *Elyonurus tripsacoides*. Inflorescence and spikelet pair.
Fig. 67. *Eragrostis barrelieri*. Plant and spikelet.
Fig. 68. *Eragrostis capillaris*. Spikelet and pedicel.
Fig. 69. *Eragrostis curtipedicillata*. Inflorescence and spikelet.
Fig. 70. *Eragrostis lugens*. Plant, with enlarged spikelet.
Fig. 71 a-b. *Erogrostis megastachya*. Inflorescence and spikelet.
Fig. 72 a-b. *Eragrostis oxylepis*. Inflorescence and spikelet.
Fig. 73. *Eragostis sessilispica*. Inflorescence and spikelet.
Fig. 74. *Eragrostis spectabilis*. Inflorescence and spikelet.
Fig. 75 a-c. *Eriochloa contracta*. Plant, spikelet and fertile floret.
Fig. 76. *Eriochloa punctata*. Spikelet.
Fig. 77. *Eriochloa sericea*. Plant, spikelet and fertile floret.
Fig. 78. *Erioneuron pilosum*. Inflorescence and spikelet.
Fig. 79. *Heteropogon contortus*. Plant and seed-bearing spikelet.
Fig. 80. *Hilaria belangeri*. Plant and two views of spikelet cluster.
Fig. 81. *Hordeum leporinum*. Inflorescence and 3 spikelets at node of rachis.
Fig. 82. *Hordeum pusillum*. Plant and spikelet.
Fig. 83. *Hordeum vulgare*. Inflorescence and 3 spikelets at node of rachis.
Fig. 84. *Leersia hexandra*. Plant and spikelet.
Fig. 85 a-b. *Leersia monandra*. Inflorescence and spikelet.
Fig. 86 a-b. *Leersia virginica*. Inflorescence and spikelet.
Fig. 87. *Leptochloa domingensis*. Inflorescence and spikelet.
Fig. 88. *Leptochloa dubia*. Inflorcscence and spikelet.
Fig. 89 a-b. *Leptochloa fascicularis*. Inflorescence and spikelet.
Fig. 90 a-b. *Leptochloa filiformis*. Inflorescence and spikelet.
Fig. 91 a-b. *Leptochloa nealleyi*. Inflorescence and spikelet.
Fig. 92. *Leptochloa uninervia*. Spikelet.
Fig. 93. *Leptoloma cognatum*. Plant and spikelet.
Fig. 94. *Limnodia arkansana*. Inflorescence (a), spikelet (b), and floret (c).
Fig. 95. *Lolium perenne*. Inflorescence (a), terminal spikelet with awnless lemmas (b), terminal spikelet with awned lemmas (c).
Fig. 96 a-b. *Manisuris altissima*. Inflorescence and spikelet pair on section of rachis.
Fig. 97 a-b. *Manisuris cylindrica*. Inflorescence and spikelet pair on section of rachis.
Fig. 98. *Monanthochloe littoralis*. Plant with staminate spikelet (a), and pistillate spikelet (b).
Fig. 99. *Muhlenbergia capillaris*. Inflorescence and spikelet with glumes separated from floret.

Fig. 100. *Muhlenbergia schreberi.* Plant and spikelet.
Fig. 101 a-b. *Neeragrostis reptans.* Pistillate florets (a), the upper with the lemma removed, and staminate florets (b), the upper with the lemmas removed.
Fig. 102. *Oplismenus setarius.* Plant and spikelet.
Fig. 103. *Oryza sativa.* Inflorescence and spikelet.
Fig. 104. *Panicum agrostoides.* Inflorescence and spikelet.
Fig. 105. *Panicum antidotale.* Plant and spikelet.
Fig. 106. *Panicum brachyantherum.* Plant, spikelet and fertile floret.
Fig. 107. *Panicum capillarioides.* Inflorescence and spikelet.
Fig. 108. *Panicum dichotomiflorum.* Inflorescence and spikelet.
Fig. 109. *Panicum fasciculatum.* Plant, spikelet and fertile floret.
Fig. 110. *Panicum filipes.* Plant and spikelet.
Fig. 111. *Panicum geminatum.* Inflorescence and spikelet.
Fig. 112. *Panicum hallii.* Plant, spikelet, and fertile floret.
Fig. 113. *Panicum hians.* Plant and spikelet.
Fig. 114. *Panicum lanuginosum.* Flowering culm and spikelet.
Fig. 115. *Panicum nodatum.* Two views of spikelet (a-b) and fertile floret (c).
Fig. 116. *Panicum obtusum.* Plant and spikelet.
Fig. 117. *Panicum oligosanthes.* Plant (autumnal phase), inflorescence (vernal phase) and spikelet.
Fig. 118. *Panicum ovinum.* Plant and spikelet.
Fig. 119. *Panicum paludivagum.* Spikelet.
Fig. 120 a-b. *Panicum reptans.* Inflorescence and spikelet.
Fig. 121. *Panicum sphaerocarpon.* Plant and spikelet.
Fig. 122. *Panicum texanum.* Inflorescence and spikelet.
Fig. 123. *Panicum virgatum.* Inflorescence, spikelet and fertile floret.
Fig. 124 a-c. *Pappophorum bicolor.* Plant (a), spikelet (b), and mature floret (c).
Fig. 125. *Pappophorum mucronulatum.* Inflorescence.
Fig. 126. *Parapholis incurva.* Plant and spikelet with section of rachis.
Fig. 127. *Paspalum dilatatum.* Inflorescence and spikelet.
Fig. 128. *Paspalum distichum.* Inflorescence and spikelet.
Fig. 129. *Paspalum floridanum.* Plant, spikelet and fertile floret.
Fig. 130. *Paspalum hartwegianum.* Spikelet.
Fig. 131 a-b. *Paspalum langei.* Inflorescence and pair of spikelets.
Fig. 132. *Paspalum lividum.* Plant and spikelet.
Fig. 133. *Paspalum monostachyum.* Inflorescence and spikelet.
Fig. 134. *Paspalum notatum.* Inflorescence.
Fig. 135 a-b. *Paspalum plicatulum.* Inflorescence and pair of spikelets.
Fig. 136. *Paspalum pubiflorum.* Inflorescence and pair of spikelets.
Fig. 137. *Paspalum setaceum.* Two inflorescence types (a-b) and two spikelet types (c-d).
Fig. 138 a-b. *Paspalum urvillei.* Plant and pair of spikelets.
Fig. 139 a-b. *Paspalum vaginatum.* Two views of spikelet.
Fig. 140. *Phalaris canariensis.* Inflorescence and spikelet.
Fig. 141. *Phalaris caroliniana.* Plant, spikelet, and fertile floret with rudiments at its base.
Fig. 142. *Phragmites communis.* Spikelet.
Fig. 143. *Poa annua.* Plant and spikelet.
Fig. 144. *Polypogon monspeliensis.* Inflorescence and spikelet.
Fig. 145. *Schedonnardus paniculatus.* Inflorescence and spikelet.
Fig. 146. *Scleropoa rigida.* Plant and spikelet.
Fig. 147. *Setaria adhaerans.* Spikelet.
Fig. 148 a-b. *Setaria firmula.* Plant and spikelet with subtending bristles.
Fig. 149. *Setaria geniculata.* Inflorescence and spikelet.
Fig. 150. *Setaria leucopila.* Plant and spikelet.
Fig. 151. *Setaria ramiseta.* Plant and spikelet.
Fig. 152. *Setaria reverchoni.* Plant and spikelet subtended by bristle.
Fig. 153. *Setaria scheelei.* Two types of panicles.

Fig. 154.   *Setaria texana.* Inflorescence.
Fig. 155.   *Sorghastrum nutans.* Plants and spikelet with pedicel of totally reduced paired spikelet.
Fig. 156.   *Sorghum halapense.* Inflorescence and spikelet pair.
Fig. 157.   *Spartina alterniflora.* Inflorescence and spikelet.
Fig. 158.   *Spartina patens.* Inflorescence.
Fig. 159 a-b.   *Spartina spartinae.* Inflorescence and spikelet.
Fig. 160.   *Sphenopholis obtusata.* Plant and spikelet.
Fig. 161.   *Sporobolus airoides.* Plant and spikelet with glumes separated from the floret.
Fig. 162.   *Sporobolus asper* var. *canovirens.* Inflorescence and spikelet.
Fig. 163.   *Sporobolus cryptandrus.* Plant and spikelet with glumes separated from the floret.
Fig. 164 a-b.   *Sporobolus poiretii.* Inflorescence and spikelet.
Fig. 165 a-b.   *Sporobolus pyramidatus.* Inflorescence and spikelet.
Fig. 166.   *Sporobolus tharpii.* Inflorescence and spikelet.
Fig. 167.   *Sporobolus virginicus.* Plant and spikelet.
Fig. 168.   *Stenotaphrum secundatum.* Plant and spikelet.
Fig. 169.   *Stipa leucotricha.* Inflorescence and spikelet.
Fig. 170.   *Trachypogon secundus.* Plant and spikelet.
Fig. 171.   *Trichloris pluriflora.* Inflorescence and spikelet.
Fig. 172.   *Trichoneura elegans.* Inflorescence and spikelet.
Fig. 173.   *Tridens albescens.* Plant, spikelet, and floret.
Fig. 174.   *Tridens congestus.* Inflorescence and spikelet.
Fig. 175.   *Tridens eragrostoides.* Inflorescence and spikelet.
Fig. 176.   *Tridens flavus.* Inflorescence and spikelet.
Fig. 177 a-b.   *Tridens muticus.* Plant and spikelet with glumes separated from the florets.
Fig. 178.   *Tridens strictus.* Spikelet.
Fig. 179.   *Triplasis purpurea.* Inflorescence and spikelet.
Fig. 180.   *Tripsacum dactyloides.* Inflorescence.
Fig. 181.   *Trisetum interruptum.* Inflorescence and spikelet.
Fig. 182.   *Triticum aestivum.* Inflorescence.
Fig. 183 a-c.   *Uniola latifolia.* Plant, spikelet and floret.
Fig. 184.   *Uniola paniculata.* Spikelet.
Fig. 185.   *Vaseyochloa multinervosa.* Plant, spikelet, floret and caryopsis.
Fig. 186.   *Vulpia octoflora.* Plant and spikelet.
Fig. 187 a-b.   *Willkommia texana.* Plant and spikelet.
Fig. 188.   *Zizaniopsis miliacea.* Inflorescence, staminate spikelet, pistillate spikelet, and caryopsis.

KEY TO THE GENERA

Leaf blades about 1 cm long; stoloniferous, mat-forming perennial with fascicled leaves and inconspicious unisexual spikelets **MONANTHOCHLOE**
Leaf blades more than 1 cm long; plants not as above
  Spikelet unisexual, the staminate and pistillate spikelets very different in appearance
    Plants monoecious, the pistillate spikelets indurate, below the staminate in a spike or 2-3 spicate branches; tall bunchgrass **TRIPSACUM**
    Plants usually dioecious, the pistillate spikelets in indurate bur-like clusters; plants low, stoloniferous **BUCHLOE**
  Spikelets perfect or if unisexual then the staminate and pistillate not strikingly different.
    Spikelets with a single perfect floret, with or without reduced florets (in *Zizaniopsis* the spikelets with a single staminate or pistillate floret) **A**
    Spikelets with 2 or more perfect florets, or if spikelets unisexual then with 2 or more staminate or pistillate florets **AA**

A

First glume larger and firmer than the lemma of the fertile floret; spikelets in combinations of 1 sessile and 1 or 2 pedicelled, the pedicelled spikelet usually reduced (in a few taxa the pedicelled spikelet reduced to the pedicel alone) **GROUP I page 8**
First glume present or absent, not as large or firm as the lemma of the fertile floret or if so then the spikelets not in combinations of 1 sessile and 1 or 2 pedicelled
  Reduced (staminate or sterile) floret present below the fertile one, with a lemma similar to the glume or glumes in texture; lemma of the fertile floret firm or indurate, glabrous and shiny, thicker than the glumes and sterile lemma; disarticulation below the glumes **GROUP II page 9**
  Reduced florets not present below the fertile one (in *Phalaris,* the one exception, disarticulation is above the glumes)
    Inflorescence a panicle or open raceme, the primary branches not spicate **GROUP III page 10**
    Inflorescence a spike, spicate raceme, or with 2 to several spicate primary branches
      Inflorescence with 2 (occasionally 1) to several primary branches **GROUP V page 12**
      Inflorescence a terminal spike or spicate raceme **GROUP VI page 13**

AA

Inflorescence a panicle or open raceme, at least some of the primary branches rebranched **GROUP IV page 10**
Inflorescence a spike or spicate raceme or with spicate primary branches
  Inflorescence with 2 (rarely 1) to several primary branches **GROUP V page 12**
  Inflorescence a terminal spike or spicate raceme **GROUP VI page 13**

GROUP 1

Spikelets awnless
  Inflorescence a single spicate raceme or of 2-3 spicate branches
    Inflorescence axis broad, flattened and thickened; pedicelled spikelet almost entirely reduced, the pedicel glabrous **MANISURIS**
    Inflorescence axis not broad, flattened and thickened; pedicelled spikelet well developed, the pedicel puberulent **ELYONURUS**
  Inflorescence a panicle with numerous branches **SORGHUM**

Spikelets awned
  Awn of fertile lemma 3-8 cm long, scabrous or pubescent; inflorescence a spicate raceme
    Perfect (awned) spikelets sessile; glumes and awns of perfect spikelets dark brown at maturity .... HETEROPOGON
    Perfect (awned) spikelets pedicelled; glumes and awns of perfect spikelets light-colored .... TRACHYPOGON
  Awn of fertile lemma 0.7-3 cm long, glabrous or scabrous; inflorescence with few to numerous branches
    Main culm terminating in numerous leafy flowering branchlets, each bearing 1-4 pedunculate flower clusters .... ANDROPOGON
    Main culm terminating in an open or contracted panicle, this without leaves or bracts
      Panicle axis less than 15 cm long or if longer then the panicle 2 cm or less broad; pedicelled spikelets reduced but present .... ANDROPOGON
      Panicle axis usually 15-30 cm long, the panicle more than 2 cm broad
        Pedicelled spikelets staminate, well developed .... SORGHUM
        Pedicelled spikelets represented by the pedicel only .... SORGHASTRUM

GROUP II

Spikelets contained in involucres of bristles or flattened spines, these disarticulating with the spikelets .... CENCHRUS
Spikelets not in involucres, the subtending bristles persistent when present
  Spikelets all or in part (those terminating branchlets) subtended by one to several slender bristles .... SETARIA
  Spikelets not subtended by bristles
    Inflorescence a spike, the spikelets partially embedded in a thick, flattened rachis; first glume present .... STENOTAPHRUM
    Inflorescence not a spike or if appearing so then spikelets lacking the first glume
      Fertile lemma firm but thin and flexible, the margins membranous and not inrolled over the palea; first glume minute or absent .... B
      Fertile lemma relatively thick and rigid, the margins inrolled over the palea; first glume present or absent .... BB

B

Inflorescence an open, much-branched panicle; spikelets on long, spreading pedicels .... LEPTOLOMA
Inflorescence of few to several racemose primary branches or a contracted panicle of sparingly rebranched racemose branches; spikelets sessile or on short, appressed pedicels .... DIGITARIA

BB

First glume absent on some or all spikelets
  Fertile lemma mucronate or short-awned; cup- or disc-like ring present at base of spikelet .... ERIOCHLOA
  Fertile lemma not mucronate or awned; cup- or disc-like ring not present at base of spikelet
    Back of sterile lemma oriented towards the rachis; spikelets narrowly oblong, about 2 mm long and less than 1 mm broad, borne singly and widely spaced in 2 rows on the rachis .... AXONOPUS
    Back of sterile lemma oriented away from the rachis; spikelets broadly ovate to oblong, closely spaced and often paired, in 2 or 4 rows on the rachis .... PASPALUM

First glume present on all spikelets
  Glumes, at least the second, awned
    First glume much shorter than the second, awnless or with a very short awn ECHINOCHLOA
    First glume about as long as the second, with an awn to 3 times the length of the body
        OPLISMENUS

  Glumes awnless
    Second glume densely long-hairy; first glume glabrous, more than half the length of the spikelet   BRACHIARIA
    Second glume not densely long-hairy; first glume less than half the length of the spikelet when the second glume pubescent
      Inflorescence of 2 to several spicate or racemose branches, the spikelets in regular rows
        Second glume and sterile lemma scabrous-pubescent with short stiff hairs   ECHINOCHLOA
        Second glume and sterile lemma scabrous
          Plant annual; rachis of inflorescence branches broadly winged, 1-2 mm wide   BRACHIARIA
          Plant perennial; rachis less than 1 mm broad   PANICUM
      Inflorescence an open or contracted panicle; perennials   LEERSIA

GROUP III

Glumes absent or rudimentary
  Spikelets perfect, strongly compressed laterally
    Spikelets 7-10 mm long; glumes vestigial; annual   ORYZA
    Spikelets less than 6 mm long; glumes absent; perennials   LEERSIA
  Spikelets unisexual, not strongly compressed; panicle large, the staminate and pistillate spikelets intermingled   ZIZANIOPSIS

Glumes, at least the second, well developed
  Glumes and lemmas awnless
    Glumes longer than the lemma
      Glumes 3-5 mm or more long; scale-like rudiments present below the fertile floret   PHALARIS
      Glumes 2 mm or less long; rudiments absent   AGROSTIS
    Glumes, at least the first, shorter than the lemma   SPOROBOLUS
  Glumes or lemmas awned
    Awn of lemma 6-10 cm long, unbranched   STIPA
    Awn of lemma less than 6 cm long or awn 3-branched
      Awn of lemma 3-branched, 1 cm or more long   ARISTIDA
      Awn of lemma unbranched
        Lemma awned from below the middle   ALOPECURUS
        Lemma awned from above the middle
          Glumes with a delicate awn exceeding the body in length   POLYPOGON
          Glumes awnless
            Glumes as long as or longer than the lemma; disarticulation below the glumes; plant annual   LIMNODEA
            Glumes, at least the first, shorter than the lemma; disarticulation above the glumes; plants perennial   MUHLENBERGIA

GROUP IV

Plants 2-6 meters tall; giant reed grasses
  Culms densely tufted, creeping rhizomes absent; leaves basal, the blades mostly 0.5-1.0 cm broad, roughened on the margins by stiff epidemal projections   CORTADERIA

Culms forming large colonies but not tufted, with stout rhizomatous bases; leaves evenly distributed on the culm, the blades 2-6 cm broad, without rough margins
    Lemmas villous, rachilla glabrous   ARUNDO
    Lemma glabrous, rachilla villous   PHRAGMITES
Plants less than 2 meters tall
    Plants dioecious; grasses of moist saline sites or drying swales and lake beds
        Plants perennial, with stout rhizomes and long, stiff leaf blades   DISTICHLIS
        Plants annual, without rhizomes but extensively stoloniferous and mat-forming; leaf blades short and soft   NEERAGROSTIS
    Plants not dioecious, rhizomatous or stoloniferous
    Lemmas 3-nerved   C
    Lemmas 5-several-nerved   CC

C

Nerves or margins of lemma pubescent, at least below, usually extending into short mucro
    Panicle 1-3 cm long, contracted, ovoid   ERIONEURON
    Panicle 4-20 cm or more long, contracted or open
        Plants annual; palea densely ciliate on upper half   TRIPLASIS
        Plants perennial; palea not ciliate on upper half   TRIDENS
Nerves and margins of lemma glabrous, not extending into mucro (see also *Tridens albescens* with glabrous but usually mucronate lemmas)   ERAGROSTIS

CC

Glumes equalling or exceeding the lower floret in length; lemmas awned
    Glumes 4-5 mm long   TRISETUM
    Glumes 2 cm or more long   AVENA
Glumes, at least the first, shorter than the lower floret
    Spikelets 2 cm or more long, strongly flattened, with keeled glumes and lemmas
        Lowermost floret or florets reduced, shorter than those in the middle of the spikelet; perennial warm-season plants   UNIOLA
        Lower floret not reduced; annual or weak perennial cool-season plants   BROMUS
    Spikelets less than 2 cm long or if this large then not strongly flattened and without keeled glumes and lemmas
        First glume short and narrow, second glume large, broad, obovate; lemmas awnless   SPHENOPHOLIS
        First and second glume not as above
            Lemma awned, mucronate or narrowly acute
                Lemma with numerous awns   PAPPOPHORUM
                Lemma with one awn
                      Spikelets more than 15 mm long; lemmas awned from a notched apex   BROMUS
                      Spikelets less than 15 mm long; lemmas acute or awned from an entire apex
                          Plant annual, infrequently over 40 cm tall   VULPIA
                          Plant perennial, usually 50-120 cm tall   FESTUCA
            Lemma awnless, obtuse or rounded at the apex
                Nerves of lemma 7-11, prominent; caryopsis oval, concavo-convex with persistent horn-like styles; moderately tall warm-season perennial   VASEYOCHLOA
                Nerves of the lemma 5-7, indistinct or only the midnerve and 2 lateral nerves prominent; caryopsis not as above; low cool-season annuals

Lemma keeled and with more or less pubescent nerves   POA
Lemma rounded on back, glabrous   SCLEROPA

GROUP V

Spikelets with a single perfect floret, with or without reduced or rudimentary florets   D

Spikelets with 2 or more perfect florets   DD

D

Inflorescence branches mostly 2-6 in a single digitate cluster at the culm apex; rudimentary floret absent or represented by a minute scale   CYNODON

Inflorescence not digitate or if so then spikelets with one or more reduced florets above the fertile one

  Stout hooked spines present on outer glumes, the spikelets in deciduous, bur-like clusters of 2-5   TRAGUS

  Stout hooked spines not present on glumes

    Main inflorescence axis bearing few to numerous spikelets at its tip

      Glumes absent; spikelets strongly compressed laterally; lemma firm, "boat-shaped"   LEERSIA

      Glumes present

        Glumes stiff, the first narrowly acute or acuminate, strongly 1-nerved   SCHEDONNARDUS

        Glumes soft, the first broad and irregularly lacerate or toothed at the apex, nerveless   WILLKOMMIA

    Main inflorescence axis not spikelet-bearing, the spikelets all on primary branches

      Spikelets without reduced or rudimentary florets; inflorescence branches erect-appressed, or somewhat spreading, never in verticels   SPARTINA

      Spikelets with one or more staminate or rudimentary florets above the perfect one

        Inflorescence branches digitate or clustered at the culm apex or in 2-3 verticels, if somewhat scattered then the branches 7 cm or more long

          Spikelets 3-5 flowered; lemmas mostly 3-awned, the lateral awns much shorter than the central awn and sometimes lacking   TRICHLORIS

          Spikelets 2-flowered (3-flowered in *C.virgata* and *C. gayana*); lemmas with a single awn   CHLORIS

        Inflorescence branches scattered on the axis, not over 4 cm long

          Plants stoloniferous and sod-forming   BUCHLOE

          Plants not stoloniferous and sod-forming   BOUTELOUA

DD

Inflorescence branches paired, digitate or clustered at the culm apex

  Glumes and lemmas awnless   ELEUSINE

  Glumes or lemmas awned

    Inflorescence branches numerous, clustered at the culm apex, 7-15 cm long   TRICHLORIS

    Inflorescence branches few, digitate, 1-5 cm long   DACTYLOCTENIUM

Inflorescence branches scattered on the axis

  Glumes much exceeding the lower floret in length; lemmas conspicuously ciliate on the margins   TRICHONEURA

  Glumes, at least the first, shorter than the lower floret; lemmas glabrous or short-ciliate on the margins

Spikelets widely spaced and mostly not overlapping on the stiffly spreading branches ERAGROSTIS *(E. sessilispica)*
Spikelets closely placed and overlapping on the branches
  Spikelets sessile or nearly so; inflorescence branches, at least some, more than 3 cm long LEPTOCHLOA
  Spikelets on stout pedicels mostly 1-3 mm long; inflorescence branches mostly 1-1.5 cm long SCLEROPOA

GROUP VI

Spikelets in capitate clusters of usually 3-5, these subsessile in the leafy portion of the plant BUCHLOE
Spikelets not as above
  Spikelets with a single floret
    Glumes bearing hooked prickles or spines TRAGUS
    Glumes not bearing prickles or spines
      Spikelets single at each node, more or less embedded in the rachis PARAPHOLIS
      Spikelets 3 at each node, not embedded in the rachis HORDEUM
  Spikelets with 2 to several florets
    Spikelets borne single at the nodes (rarely paired at 1 or 2 nodes)
      Spikelets oriented edgewise to the rachis, the first glume absent except in the terminal spikelet LOLIUM
      Spikelets not oriented edgewise to the rachis, both glumes present on all spikelets
        Spikelets sessile, glumes thick and indurate; annual TRITICUM
        Spikelets short-pedicelled; glumes not indurate
          Lemmas thick, with several indistinct nerves; rhizomatous perennial DISTICHLIS
          Lemmas thin, 3-nerved; stoloniferous annual NEERAGROSTIS
    Spikelets mostly 2-3 at each node
      Spikelets disarticulating in clusters (below the glumes); plants low, stoloniferous HILARIA
      Spikelets disarticulating above the glumes; bunchgrasses with moderately tall culms and no stolons ELYMUS

GENERA AND SPECIES

1. AGROSTIS Bentgrass

Annuals and perennials with open or contracted panicles of small one-flowered spikelets.

A genus of about 100 species, distributed mainly in the temperate and cool regions of the world. Represented in Texas by four native and four introduced species.

*1. AGROSTIS HIEMALIS (Walt.) B.S.P. WINTER BENTGRASS. (Fig. 2). Native cool season annual or weak perennial with open, delicate panicle of small spikelets. Abundant in early spring as an invader on disturbed sites. An insignificant grass of slight forage value.

2. ALOPECURUS Foxtail

Annuals and perennials with slender, cylindrical, contracted panicles. Spikelets one-flowered, disarticulating below the glumes. Glumes subequal, awnless, united at the extreme base. Lemmas awned from the middle or below, the awn delicate. Palea absent.

About 25 species, these mostly in cold and temperate regions of the northern hemisphere. Represented in Texas by two annuals, one native and one adventative.

1. ALOPECURUS CAROLINIANUS Walt. CAROLINA FOXTAIL. Native cool-season annual, usually growing as a weed on moist, open, disturbed sites such as ditches and roadbanks. Not definitely recorded for the Coastal Bend but collected as far south as Gonzales County and to be expected in our area.

---
*Species known to occur on the Welder Wildlife Refuge.

Fig. 2. *Agrostis hiemalis*. Plant and spikelet.

3. ANDROPOGON Bluestem

Stout warm-season perennials (ours), with usually broad, flat, rather coarse blades. Inflorescense of spicate branches, these borne singly or in groups, on lateral peduncles or in a terminal leafless cluster. Spikelets in pairs of one sessile and perfect, and one pedicelled and staminate or rudimentary (represented by pedicel only in a few species). Disarticulation at the base of the sessile spikelet and at the nodes of the inflorescence axis or branch, the spikelet pair usually falling together with the rachis joint (node and internode) and pedicel.

As herein treated, this genus includes some 200 or more species, these for the most part confined to the tropics and subtropics. With the exception of the U. S. agrostologists, most systematists of the world segregrate this group of grasses into a number of genera. Following this policy, the 17 native Texas species would be referrable to three genera, *Andropogon, Schizachyrium* and *Bothriochloa,* and the 7 introduced species to 2 genera, *Bothriochloa* and *Dichanthium.*

KEY TO THE SPECIES

Spikelet-bearing branchlets numerous but borne singly on slender bracteate peduncles *A. scoparius*

Spikelet-bearing branches in pairs or clusters at the ends of bracteate peduncles or in a leafless terminal cluster

    Pedicels and upper rachis joints flattened, with a deep medial groove or broad membranous central area; inflorescence a terminal leafless cluster of few to numerous floriferous branches **A**

    Pedicels and rachis joints flattened or terete, without a medial groove or membranous area; inflorescences on lateral peduncles or in a terminal cluster of not more than 10 branches **AA**

A

Pedicelled spikelets about as large as the sessile ones; introduced species

    Axis of the inflorescence typically shorter than the lower branches; inflorescence branches usually 3-10 *A. ischaemum*

    Axis of the inflorescence typically longer than the lower branches; inflorescence branches usually more than 10 *A. intermedius*

Pedicelled spikelets reduced, neuter, mostly represented by a glume only; native species

    Spikelets 4.5-7.5 mm long; awn of lemma 2.0-2.8 cm long

        First glume of all sessile spikelets with glandular pit; panicle axis less than 5 cm long; primary panicle branches mostly 2-7; upper culm nodes glabrous or short-puberulent; blades mostly 2-5 mm broad *A. hybridus*

        First glume with or without glandular pit; panicle axis usually more than 5 cm long; primary panicle branches typically more than 7; culm nodes usually densely pubescent; blades often more than 5 mm broad *A. barbinodis*

    Spikelets 4.5 mm or less long; awn less than 2 cm long

        Panicles 5-9, occasionally -13, cm long; glumes ovate, dull green and commonly with a whitish waxy bloom; pollen averaging 34-37 microns in diameter *A. saccharoides* var. *torreyanus*

        Panicles of the larger culms 10-20 cm long; glumes narrowly ovate, shiny green; pollen averaging 39-42 microns in diameter *A. saccharoides* var. *longipaniculata*

AA

Pedicelled spikelets vestigial or absent and represented by the pedicel alone

    Sessile spikelets 5-7 mm long; rachis of inflorescence branches stiff and straight   *A. ternarius*

    Sessile spikelets 4 mm or less long; rachis of inflorescence branches slender and flexuous

        Inflorescence broom-like, profusely branched and rebranched, the terminal sheaths and peduncles greatly reduced and crowded; plants large and coarse   *A. glomeratus*

        Inflorescence not broom-like, the panicle branches moderately rebranched; plants not large and coarse   *A. virginicus*

Pedicelled spikelets large, well developed, usually staminate

    Sessile spikelets 6-10 mm long awned; culm nodes glabrous   *A. gerardi*

    Sessile spikelets less than 5 mm long; sessile spikelet of lowermost one or two pairs on each branch awnless; culm nodes pubescent.

        First glume with an irregular line of hairs below the tip; plants erect, not developing creeping stoloniferous culms   *A. sericeus*

        First glume not with a line of hairs below the tip; long stoloniferous culms usually developed

            Inflorescence axis and peduncles finely pubescent   *A. aristatus*

            Inflorescence axis and peduncles glabrous   *A. annulatus*

1. ANDROPOGON ANNULATUS Forsk. (*Dichanthium annulatum* (Forsk.) Stapf). KLEBERG BLUESTEM. (Fig. 3). Introduced pasture grass, established here and there on the Gulf Coast from experimental pasture seedings.

*2. ANDROPOGON ARISTATUS Poir. (*A. nodosum* (Willem.) Nash, *Dichanthium nodosum* Willem., *Dichanthium aristatum* (Poir.) C. E. Hubb.). ANGLETON BLUESTEM. An introduced forage grass that has been widely seeded along the coast and in South Texas under the name of *Andropogon nodosum*. It has persisted in some native pastures and is well established in many areas along roadway, ditches and tank dams.

*3. ANDROPOGON BARBINODIS Lag. (including U. S. plants previously referred to *A. perforatus* Trin.; *Bothriochloa barbinodis* Herter). CANE BLUESTEM. (Fig. 4). Tall, rather coarse native bunchgrass, particularly adapted to loose calciferous soils of the semi-arid Southwest and northern Mexico.

Cane bluestem supplies a considerable amount of range forage in Central and Western Texas, but on the Gulf Coast it is infrequent and relatively unimportant. Plants with glandular-pitted glumes have been referred to as "pinhole bluestem," a name that has been applied indiscriminately to plants of *A. hybridus*, *A. edwardsianus* Gould and *A. altus* Hitchc.

*4. ANDROPOGON GERARDI Vitman (*A. furcatus* Muhl., *A. provincilis* Lam.). BIG BLUESTEM. (Fig. 5). Tall native bunchgrass, once widely distributed in the Coastal Bend area but now limited to relict areas and regions of light-grazing pressure. This species grows on all well-drained sites and is an excellent forage grass. Relict stands have persisted in the Welder Wildlife Refuge along the banks of the Aransas River, mostly in the protection of shrubs.

*5. ANDROPOGON GLOMERATUS (Walt.) B.S.P. BUSHY BLUESTEM. (Fig. 6). Tall coarse native bunchgrass, present along ditches, swales, spillways and other poorly drained sites. Well adapted to relatively sterile disturbed sites. Of poor grazing value.

*6. ANDROPOGON HYBRIDUS Gould. (*Bothriochloa hybridus* (Gould) Gould). HYBRID BLUESTEM. (Fig. 7). A native perennial bunchgrass that is similar to *A. barbinodis* but with shorter, more slender culms, narrow leaf blades, smaller panicles with a shorter inflorescence axis and fewer branches, and glabrous or minutely puberulent culm nodes. A shallow glandular pit is present above the center of the first glume of all sessile spikelets.

Hybrid bluestem is occasional in low-land areas along the Coast but is much more abundant in the upper portion of the South Texas Plains. It is especially well adapted to old ditches, roadway and similar sites and is of fair forage value where sufficiently abundant.

7. ANDROPOGON INTERMEDIUS R. Br. *(Bothriochloa intermedia* (R. Br.) A. Camus). AUSTRALIAN BLUESTEM. (Fig. 8). Introduced bunchgrass, generally similar to *A. ischaeum* but larger, with a longer panicle axis, and with numerous panicle branches. In our strains of *A. intermedius* at least some of the sessile spikelets have glandular glume pits, whereas in *A. ischaemum* the glume pits never are present. Trial seedings of this species have been made on the Coastal Prairie but it is infrequent outside of cultivation.

8. ANDROPOGON ISCHAEMUM L. var. *songaricus* Rupr. KING RANCH BLUESTEM. (Fig. 9). Introduced from Asia on the King Ranch and probably elsewhere in the state, this grass has spread along roadsides, waterways and other disturbed sites almost throughout Texas. It is a good seeder on disturbed soils and also spreads by decumbent stoloniferous culms. Of only poor to fair forage value, King Ranch bluestem is of most value in primary establishment of vegetation on denuded pastures and in the regrassing cultivated areas.

9. ANDROPOGON SACCHAROIDES Swartz. *(Bothrichloa saccharoides* Rydb.).

*9a. var. *longipaniculata* Gould. LONGSPIKE SILVER BLUESTEM. (Fig. 10). This tall bunchgrass is frequent on fine-textured upland soils where drainage is relatively good. It is common on roadsides and field borders. In the Coastal Bend area this grass is rated as excellent for forage and does not persist in heavily grazed pastures.

*9b. var. *torreyanus* (Steud.) Hack. SILVER BLUESTEM. (Fig. 11). One of the dominant native forage grasses of central, northern and western Texas. In the eastern and coastal sections of the state, however, it is relatively infrequent and for the most part present only on roadbanks, graded or filled railroad right of ways and other well-drained, moderately disturbed sites.

*10. ANDROPOGON SCOPARIUS Michx. *(Schizachyrium scoparium* (Michx.) Nash) A widespread native perennial, present in many intergrading forms and varieties throughout the United States, except in the Far West.

In the Texas Coastal Bend region this species is represented by var. *littoralis* (Nash) Hitchc. (Fig. 12), commonly known as seacoast bluestem. This variety has well-developed rhizomes and more or less densely pubescent inflorescence rachis joints and pedicels. Seacoast bluestem is particularly well adapted to the deep sandy sites of the Nueces soil series. In sandy areas where grazing has been light, this usually is the dominant forage species. It is considered an excellent forage grass.

Plants of *A. scoparius* on fine-textured clay-loam sites of the Coastal Bend area have in the past been referred to var. *frequens* F. T. Hubb., (Fig. 13), the "little bluestem" of the interior tall-grass prairies. On the basis of our present knowledge of the species, however, the Coastal Bend plants cannot be satisfactorily segregated into two varieties.

*11. ANDROPOGON SERICEUS R. Br. *(Dichanthium sericeum* (R. Br.) A. Camus). SILKY BLUESTEM (Fig. 14) An introduced bunchgrass, promoted at one time as an "improved" forage grass. Scattered stands have persisted on many sites from early seedlings, with best establishment along roadways and similar disturbed areas. This now is rated only "fair" as a forage plant.

12. ANDROPOGON TERNARIUS Michx. SPLITBEARD BLUESTEM (Fig. 15). A native bunchgrass that is present in dense stands in the open woodlands of East Texas but which is infrequent on the coastal prairie. In the Coastal Bend area it is occasional on coarse-textured, well-drained soils.

13. ANDROPOGON VIRGINICUS L. BROOMSEDGE BLUESTEM. Similar to *A. glomeratus* in general appearance but with shorter, less robust culms, and with smaller, less densely flowered inflorescences. Broomsedge bluestem is occasional on sterile or shallow soils. It frequently grows with *A. glomeratus* but tends to occupy higher, better drained sites. Both species are relatively unpalatable to livestock.

Fig. 3. *Andropogon annulatus*. Inflorescence and spikelet.

Fig. 4. *Andropogon barbinodis*. Inflorescence and spikelet pair.

Fig. 5. *Andropogon gerardi*. Plant, spikelet pair and spikelet.

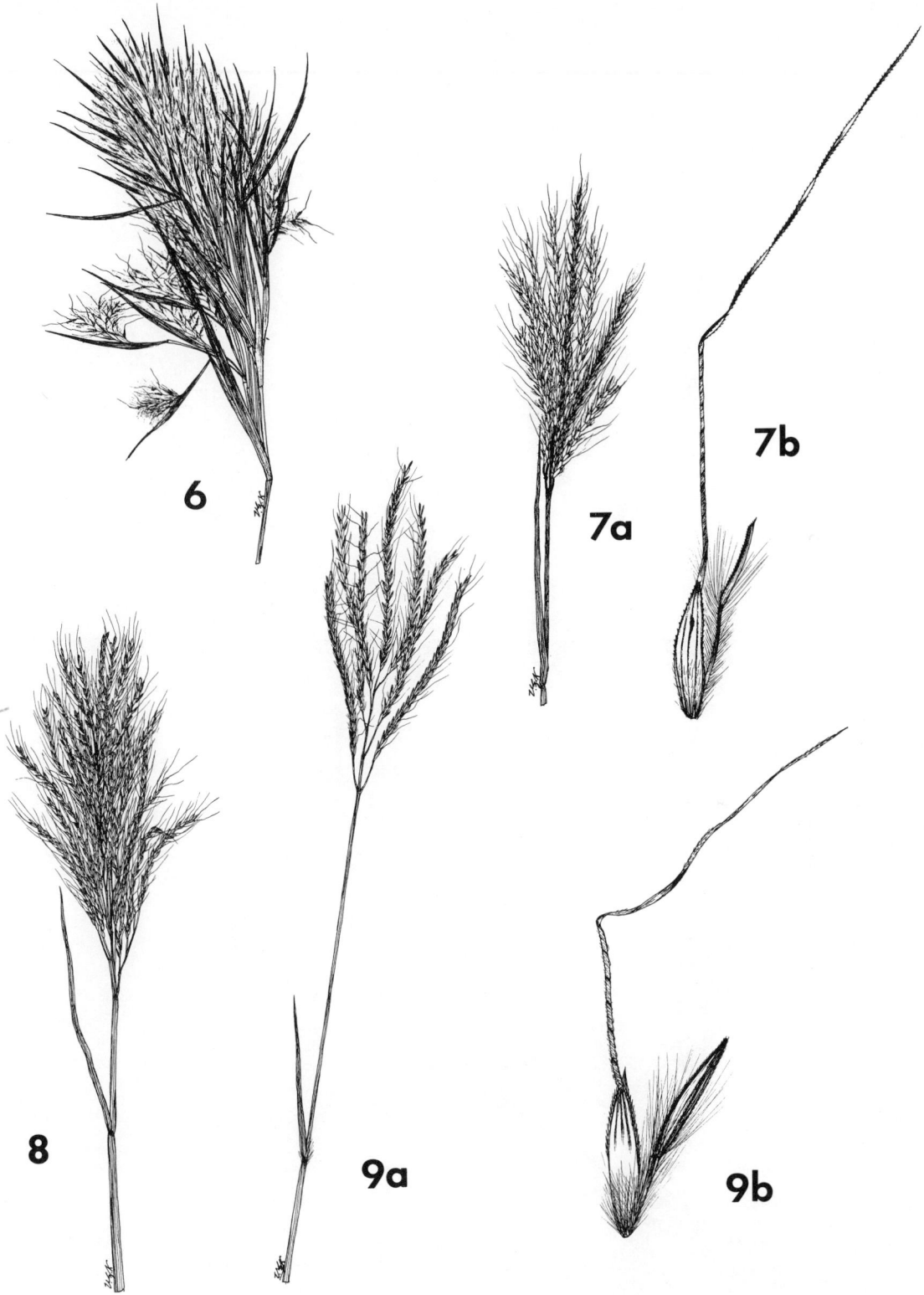

Fig. 6. *Andropogon glomeratus*. Inflorescence.
Fig. 7 a-b. *Andropogon hybridus*. Inflorescence and spikelet pair.
Fig. 8. *Andropogon intermedius*. Inflorescence.
Fig. 9 a-b. *Andropogon ischaemum* var. *songaricus*. Inflorescence and spikelet pair.

Fig. 10. *Andropogon saccharoides* var. *longipaniculata*. Inflorescence and spikelet pair.

Fig. 11. *Andropogon saccharoides* var. *torreyanus*. Inflorescence and spikelet pair.

Fig. 12. *Andropogon scoparius* var. *littoralis*. Raceme and spikelet pair.

Fig. 13. *Andropogon scoparius* var. *frequens*. Plant and spikelet pair.

Fig. 14 a-b. *Andropogon sericeus*. Inflorescence and spikelet pair.
Fig. 15 a-b. *Andropogon ternarius*. Inflorescence and spikelet pair.

4. ARISTIDA Threeawn

Grasses of temperate and subtropical regions of the world, well represented in southwestern United States and with some 36 species reported for Texas. All of our aristidas are native warm-season grasses of low forage value; many are weedy annuals. *Aristida* is placed in the monotypic tribe Aristideae by most systematists but relationships of the genus are obscure.

KEY TO THE SPECIES

First glume equal to or slightly shorter than the second; plants annual
    Articulation (joint) present at apex of awn column; awns coiled at base   *A. desmantha*
    Articulation not present at apex of awn column; awns not or only slightly coiled at base
        Awns 2.5 cm or less long; inflorescence spicate   *A. intermedia*
        Awns mostly 4 cm or more long; inflorescence not spicate at maturity   *A. oligantha*
First glume usually ½ or less as long as the second; plants perennial
    Lemmas 7-8 mm long   *A. roemeriana*
    Lemmas 9 mm or more long
        Awns 4-8 cm or more long; second glume usually 15-25 mm long but occasionally shorter; lemmas usually 14-16 mm long including the short and stout awn column   *A. longiseta*
        Awns mostly 3-4.5 cm long; glumes rarely over 15 mm long; lemmas 9-12 mm long including the slender awn column   *A. purpurea*

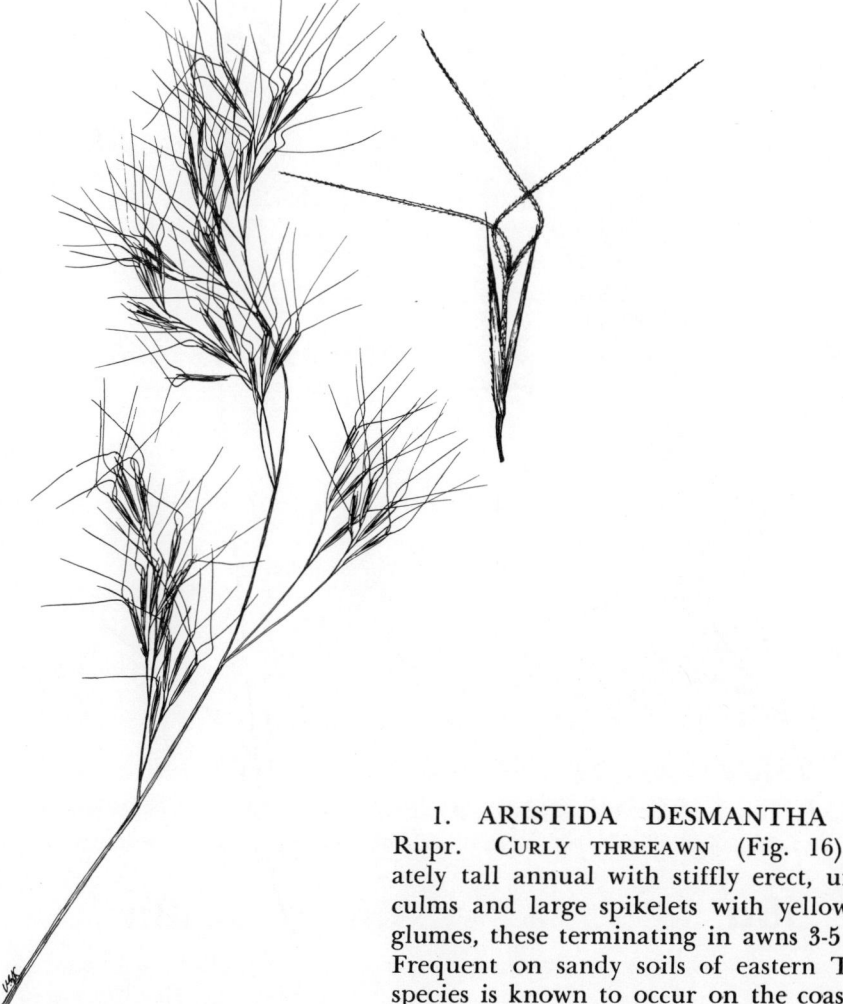

1. ARISTIDA DESMANTHA Trin. & Rupr. CURLY THREEAWN (Fig. 16). Moderately tall annual with stiffly erect, unbranched culms and large spikelets with yellowish-brown glumes, these terminating in awns 3-5 mm long. Frequent on sandy soils of eastern Texas, this species is known to occur on the coastal prairie but has not been recorded in the Coastal Bend region.

Fig. 16. *Aristida desmantha*. Inflorescence and spikelet.

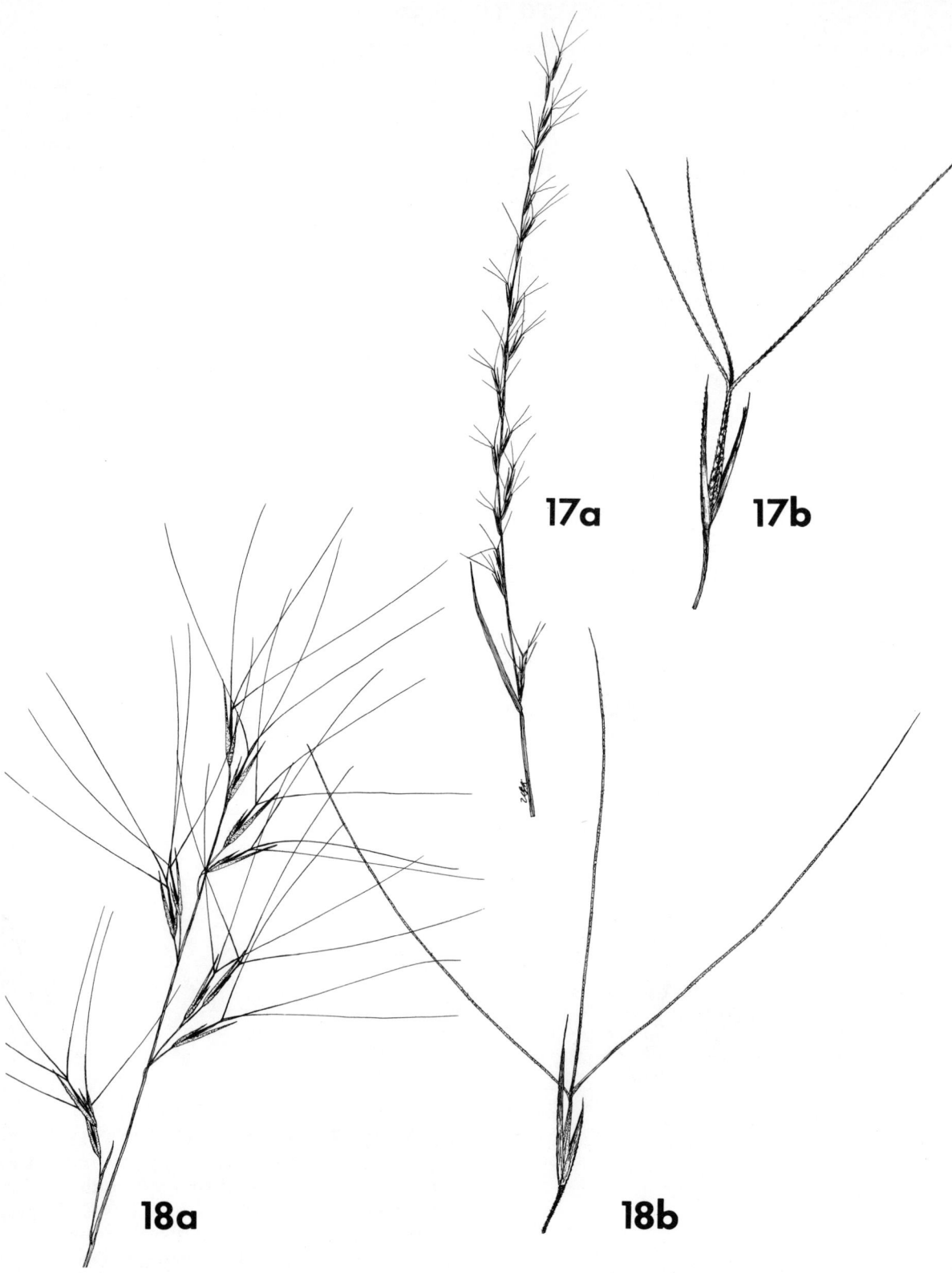

Fig. 17 a-b. *Aristida intermedia*. Inflorescence and spikelet.
Fig. 18 a-b. *Aristida longiseta*. Inflorescence and spikelet.

Fig. 19. *Aristida oligantha*. Plant.

*2. ARISTIDA INTERMEDIA Scribn. & Ball. (Fig. 17). Low, tufted short-lived annual with slender culms and narrow blades. Of occasional occurrence on disturbed sites, mostly in sand. Coastal Bend grasses referrable to this taxon were included in *Aristida longespica* Poir. var. *geniculata* (Raf.) Fern. in "Flowering plants and ferns of the Texas Coastal Bend counties" (Jones *et al.* 1961) and the recent checklist of Texas plants (Gould, 1962). Marshall Johnston is of the opinion (personal communication) that the south Texas plants of this complex, including those of the Coastal Bend, may represent an undescribed species.

Fig. 20. *Aristida purpurea*. Plant and spikelet.

Fig. 21. *Aristida roemeriana.* Inflorescence.

*3. ARISTIDA LONGISETA Steud. RED THREEAWN (Fig. 18). Low tufted perennial with leaves mostly in the basal clump. Ligule a minute ring of hairs. Awns reddish-purple at maturity. Frequent in overgrazed pastures, especially around ant beds, but only occasional on good condition ranges. Of low grazing value.

*4. ARISTIDIA OLIGANTHA Michx. PRAIRIE THREEAWN (Fig. 19). Summer annual with wiry, usually branched culms and few-flowered inflorescences of large spikelets. Abundant in overgrazed pastures on all upland sites. Plants with little or no forage value.

*5. ARISTIDA PURPUREA Nutt. PURPLE THREEAWN (Fig. 20). Similar to *A. longiseta* but with shorter glumes and usually shorter awns. Both species are widespread on the semi-arid rangelands of the Southwest. On the Texas Coastal Plain and in southern Texas *A. purpurea* is replaced by the very similar and closely related *A. roemeriana*.

*6. ARISTIDA ROEMERIANA Scheele. ROEMER THREEAWN (Fig. 21). Similar to *A. purpurea* but with smaller and more delicate spikelets and usually shorter awns. This is the dominant grass on many heavily overgrazed areas in the Coastal Bend region. Like the preceeding two species, this is a weak perennial with little or no forage value.

5. ARUNDO

A small genus of tall, stout reed-grasses, widely distributed in the tropics and subtropics of the world. Only one species, *A. donax*, has been introduced into the United States.

*1 ARUNDO DONAX L. GIANT REED (Fig. 22). Common throughout central and southern Texas along ditches and waterways, frequently planted along highway bridge approaches to prevent soil erosion. Giant reed flowers in late summer and fall, producing large plumose panicles. It is doubtful that fertile seed is ever produced on our plants, and propogation apparently is entirely by rhizomes and cuttings.

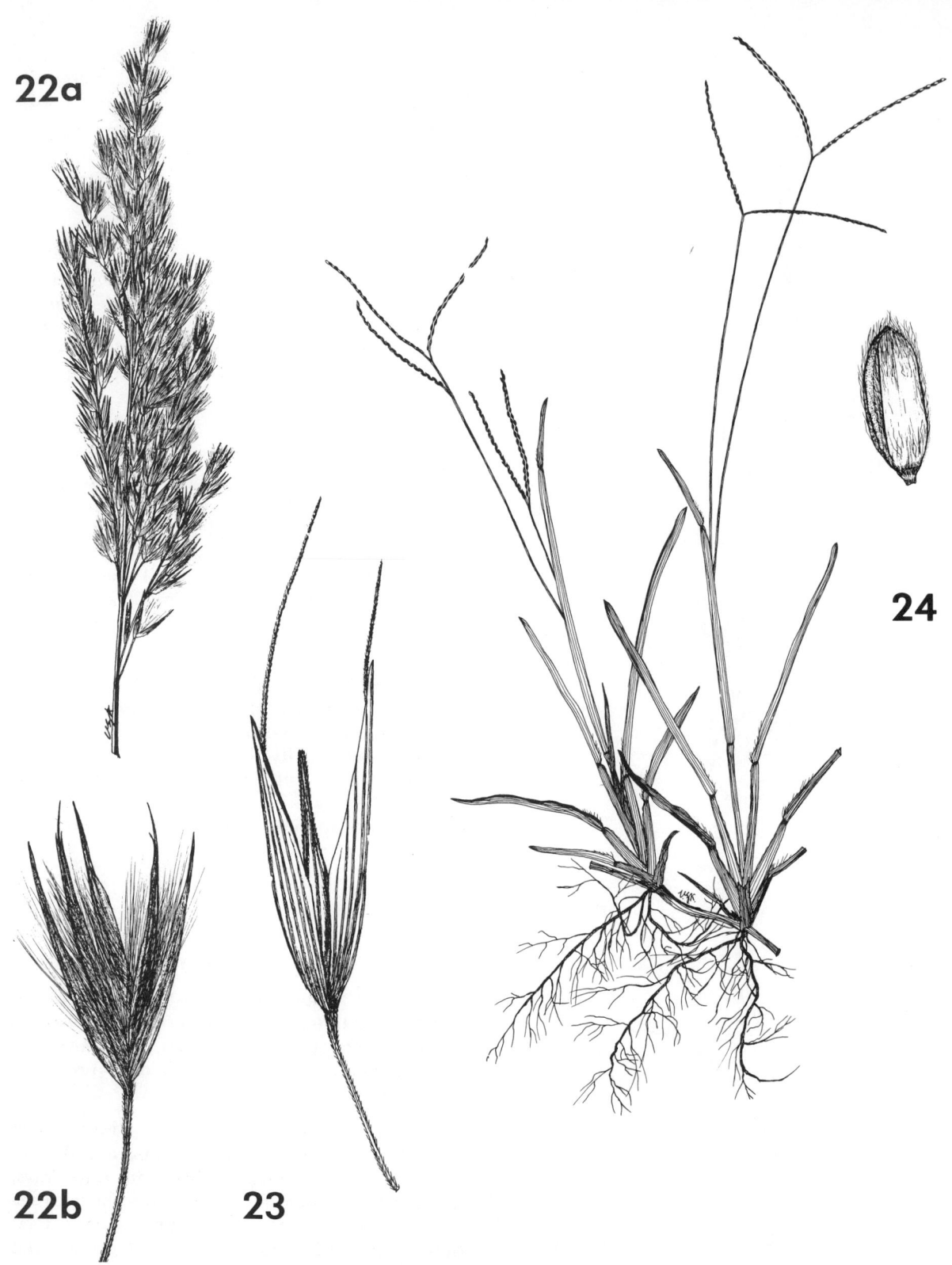

Fig. 22 a-b. *Arundo donax*. Branch of inflorescence and spikelet.
Fig. 23. *Avena fatua* var. *sativa*. Spikelet.
Fig. 24. *Axonopus affinis*. Plant and spikelet.

6. AVENA Oat

A genus of about 50 species, these native to the temperate regions of the Eastern Hemisphere.

1. AVENA FATUA L. Cool-season annual with broad flat blades and loose, few-flowered inflorescences of large spikelets. Glumes thin, several-nerved, longer than the florets. Lemmas firmer than the glumes and usually bearing a stout dorsal awn.

KEY TO THE VARIETIES

Lemmas with stiff, usually brown hairs on the dorsal surface; spikelets usually 3-flowered; awns of lemma stout, well developed, geniculate *A. fatua* var. *fatua*
Lemma glabrous; spikelets usually 2-flowered; awn of lemma irregularly developed or absent, not geniculate *A. fatua* var. *sativa*

1a. var *fatua*. WILD OAT. A weed of roadside and waste places, infrequent in our area.

1b. var. *sativa* (L.) Haussk. COMMON OAT (Fig. 23). Grown as a cereal crop throughout the Coastal Bend area and frequent as an escape on roadside and field borders.

7. AXONOPUS Carpetgrass

A New World genus of about 50 species, these mainly in the tropics. Three species native to the United States, two in Texas.

1. AXONOPUS AFFINIS Chase. COMMON CARPETGRASS (Fig. 24). Low mat-forming stoloniferous warm-season perennial; inflorescence of 2-4 slender, spicate branches, these 2-10 cm long and racemose on the main axis. This grass is frequent in coastal East Texas but as yet has not been reported from the Coastal Bend region.

8. BOUTELOUA Grama

Annuals and perennials with inflorescences of one to numerous short, unilateral branches, these bearing one to numerous closely placed, sessile or subsessile spikelets on either side of a flattened rachis. The spikelets have a single fertile floret and 1-3 reduced or rudimentary florets above. Our species are native warm-season perennials.

KEY TO THE SPECIES

Spikelets mostly 2-7 per branch, inflorescence branches deciduous as a whole
  Inflorescence branches 10 or less per culm
    Glumes glabrous (the midnerve often scabrous) *B. filiformis*
    Glumes hirsute, at least near the base *B. rigidiseta*
  Inflorescence branches 20-50 per culm *B. curtipendula*
Spikelets 15-50 per branch; inflorescence branches persistent, the spikelets disarticulating above the glumes
  Glumes hispid with pustulate-based hairs; rachis of inflorescence branch extended as a stout projection or point beyond the insertion of the terminal spikelet *B. hirsuta*
  Glumes glabrous; rachis of inflorescence branch not conspicuously extended beyond the insertion of the terminal spikelet
    Plant annual; rudiment with broad membranous lobes of tissue between the awns *B. barbata*
    Plant perennial; rudiment without membranous lobes of tissue between the awns *B. trifida*

1. BOUTELOUA BARBATA Lag. SIX WEEKS GRAMA. Low tufted annual with numerous, usually geniculate-spreading culms. Inflorescence branches mostly 2-5 (occasionally more) per culm, bearing numerous small closely-placed pectinate spikelets. Six weeks grama is an inconspicuous, short-lived weedy grass of the Southwest that occurs sparingly in the southern portion of our area.

Fig. 25. *Bouteloua curtipendula* var. *curtipendula*. Plant, glumes and spikelet with glumes removed.

Fig. 26. *Bouteloua filiformis*. Plant.

Fig. 27. *Bouteloua hirsuta*. Plant.

*2. BOUTELOUA CURTIPENDULA (Michx.) Torr. SIDEOATS GRAMA (Fig. 25). Plants mostly 40-90 cm tall, with flat, moderately broad blades and culms developed singly or in small clusters from slender creeping rhizomes. Inflorescence branches about 1 cm long, usually bearing 2-9 glabrous spikelets.

Occasional throughout the Coastal Bend region on several soil types, perhaps most frequent on clay and sandy loam sites. Sideoats grama is an excellent forage plant but in our region is seldom sufficiently abundant to be of much forage significance. Our plants are referrable to the var. *curtipendula*.

3. BOUTELOUA FILIFORMIS (Fourn.) Griffiths. SLENDER GRAMA (Fig. 26). Low, tufted perennial with narrow flat blades and narrow, few-flowered inflorescences. Inflorescence branches mostly bearing 6-10 spikelets. Widespread in southwestern United States and northern Mexico, slender grama occurs in the southwestern portion of the Coastal Bend area.

*4. BOUTELOUA HIRSUTA Lag. HAIRY GRAMA (Fig. 27). Tufted short-lived perennial, with narrow, flat blades and culms mostly 30-70 cm tall. The inflorescence branches bear 20 to 40 or more closely placed, pectinately spreading spikelets. The rachis of the spikelet-bearing branch is conspicuously extended beyond the terminal spikelet as a naked pointed stipe. The name "hairy grama" apparently is based on the presence of stiff, pustulate-based hairs on the glumes.

Hairy grama grows only on sandy and loam soils and is most frequent on well-drained sites. It is rated as an "increaser" of only fair forage value. The plants of our area frequently are viviparous in the early summer.

*5. BOUTELOUA RIGIDISETA (Steud.) Hitchc. TEXAS GRAMA (Fig. 28). Tufted weak perennial, with slender culms mostly 15-40 cm tall and short narrow flat leaf blades in a based clump. The short deciduous inflorescence branches bear usually 3-5 spikelets in a bristly wedge-shaped cluster. Texas grama is frequent on clay and clay loams, being most abundant on disturbed sites and increasing under heavy grazing. Although classed as a warm-season grass, it first flowers early in the spring.

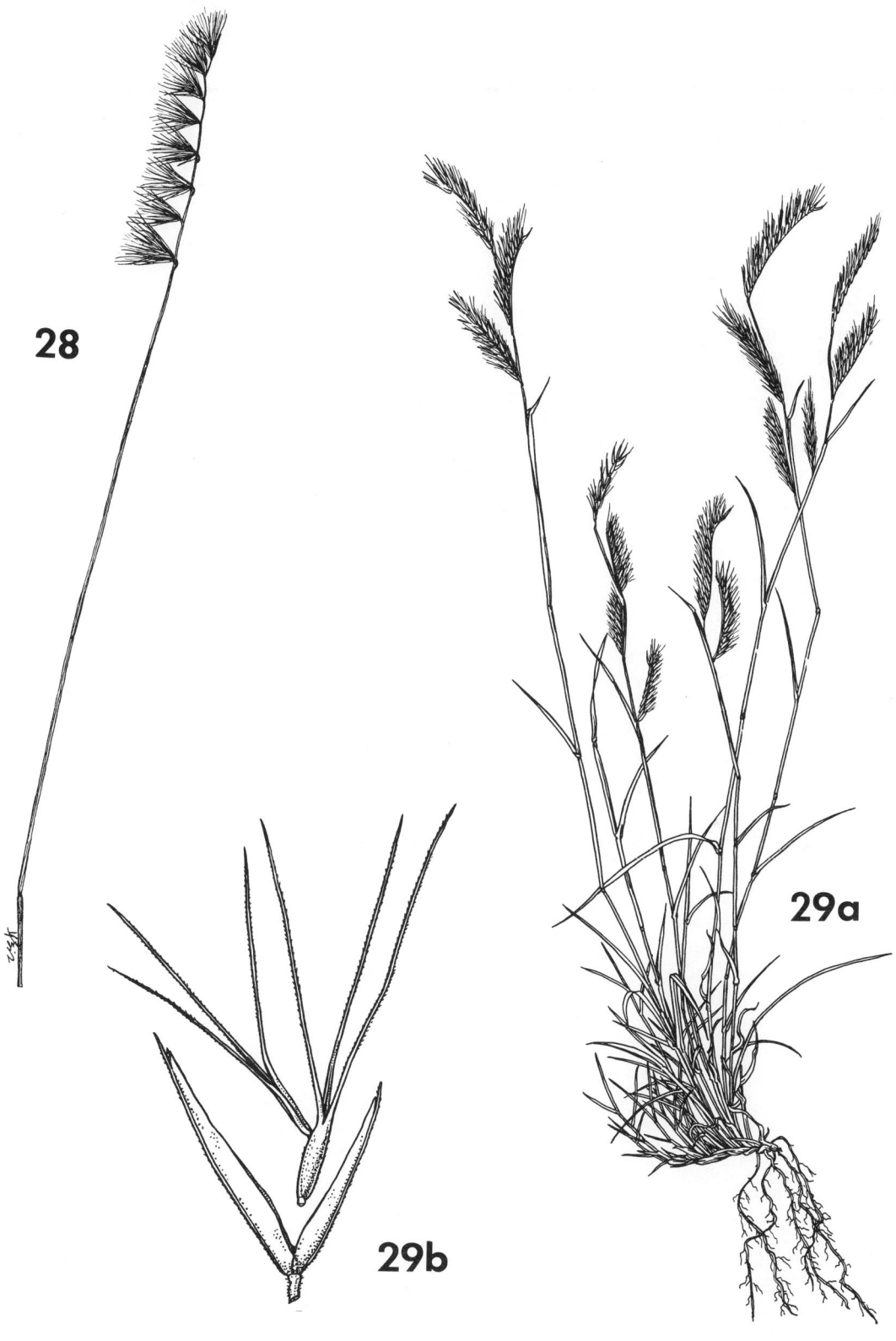

Fig. 28. *Bouteloua rigidiseta*. Inflorescence.
Fig. 29 a-b. *Bouteloua trifida*. Plant and spikelet with glumes and florets separated.

6. **BOUTELOUA TRIFIDA** Thurb. RED GRAMA (Fig. 29). Low tufted perennial with culms mostly 10 to 40 cm tall. Leaves usually 10 cm or less long and 1.5 mm or less broad. Inflorescence branches mostly 3-7, with numerous appressed spikelets. Lemma 2-3 mm long, bearing 3 awns 4-9 mm long. Rudiment about 1 mm long, with awns about as long as those of the lemma. Native warm-season perennial. Typically a plant of dry rock or sandy sites of the Southwest, red grama is only sparingly present in the Coastal Bend area. Of fair to poor forage value, this grass persists under heavy grazing and in very dry sites.

9. BRACHIARIA Signalgrass

Low spreading annuals and perennials, mostly with stolons and broad flat leaf blades. A tropical-subtropical genus of about 20 species. The two species of our area are the only ones native to the United States.

KEY TO THE SPECIES

Second glume and sterile lemma conspicuously hispid; leaf blades mostly 3-5 mm broad

B. ciliatissima

Second glume and sterile lemma glabrous; leaf blades, at least some, 7-15 mm or more broad

B. platyphylla

*1. **BRACHIARIA CILIATISSIMA** (Buckl.) Chase. FRINGED SIGNALGRASS (Fig. 30). Plants with stout, spreading, leafy stolons that have short internodes and swollen nodes. Leaves moderately to densely hairy, the blades short, stiff, widely spreading, mostly 3-5 mm broad. Inflorescences small, few-flowered, on slender erect culms with bearded nodes. Spikelets about 4 mm long. Margins of the second glume and sterile lemma hispid with hairs about 1 mm long. Shorter hairs present on and between the other nerves.

Native warm-season perennial. Frequent on sandy and sandy loam soils, this grass sometimes is referred to as "sandhill grass". It functions as a soil binder in sandy area subject to wind erosion and provides fair forage during periods of vigorous growth. In our area fringed signalgrass is most abundant on fine sand of the Nueces series. It usually is associated with *Setaria firmula*.

*2. **BRACHIARIA PLATYPHYLLA** (Griseb.) Nash. BROADLEAF SIGNALGRASS (Fig. 31). Culms stoloniferous, weak and spreading. Leaves relatively thick, glabrous, the blades 6-18 mm broad. Inflorescence with usually 2-6 widely spaced branches. Spikelets glabrous, ovate, 4-4.5 mm long, with a short blunt first glume and subequal second glume and sterile lemma.

Native warm-season annual, growing mainly on disturbed soils in moist open sites.

10. BROMUS Brome

A genus of over 100 species, with about 25 native to the United States and many others introduced or adventative. Primarily adapted to temperate and cool-temperate regions, the bromes of southern United States grow as cool-season plants.

Grasses of this genus characteristically have large, several-flowered spikelets borne in open panicles. Many have closed leaf-sheaths. Disarticulation of the spikelet is above the glumes and the caryopsis typically is adherent to the lemma and palea.

KEY TO THE SPECIES

Glumes and lemmas sharply keeled; lemmas awnless or with an awn 1-3 mm long; larger lemmas 1-1.5 cm long

B. willdenowii

Glumes and lemmas rounded on the back; lemmas with an awn 5-7 mm long; lemmas less than 1 cm long

B. texensis

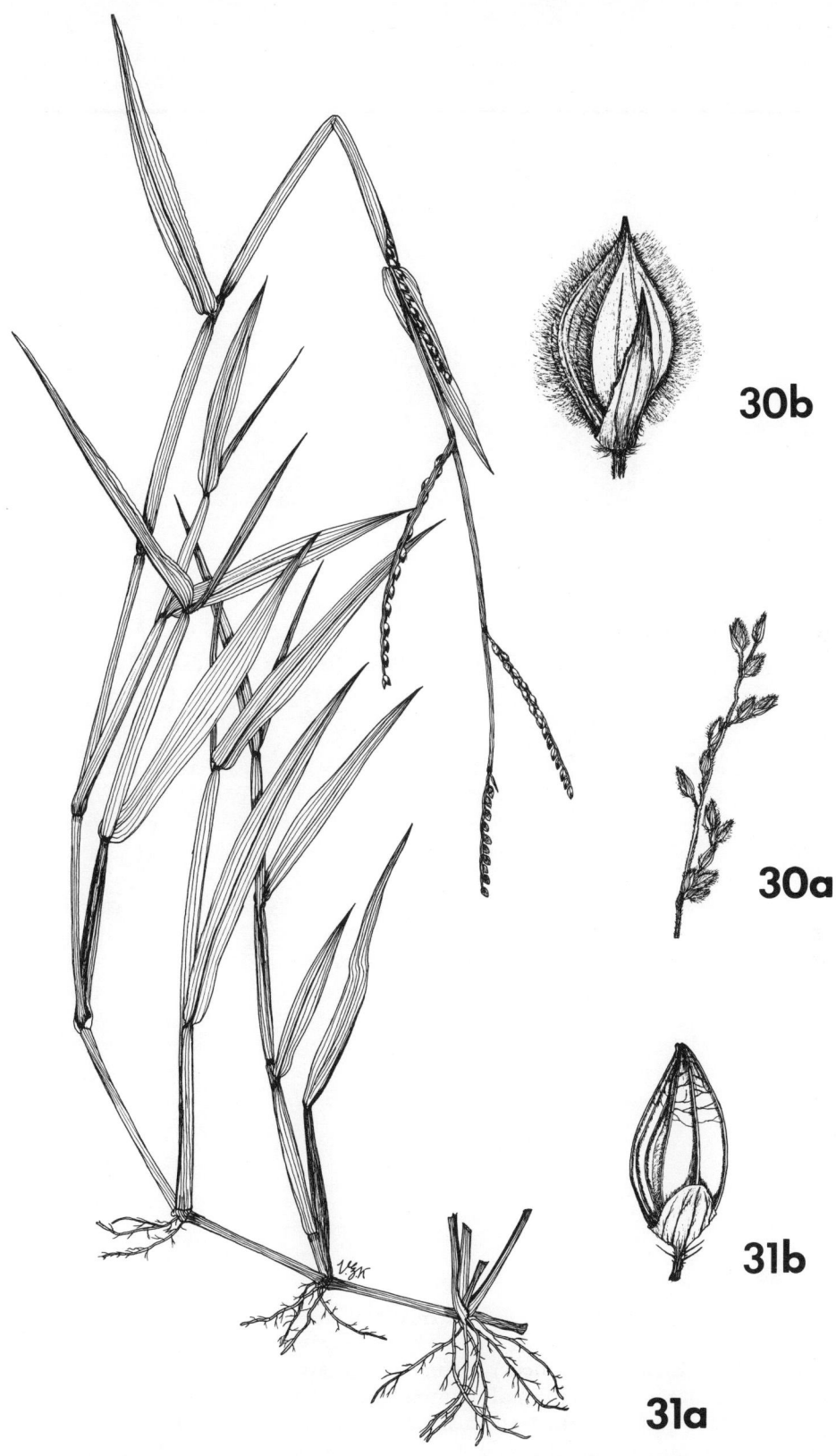

Fig. 30 a-b. *Brachiaria ciliatissima*. Inflorescence and spikelet.
Fig. 31 a-b. *Brachiaria platyphylla*. Plant and spikelet.

Fig. 32. *Bromus texensis*. Inflorescence and spikelet.

*1. BROMUS TEXENSIS (Shear) Hitchc. TEXAS BROME (Fig. 32). Culms in small clumps, mostly 30-60 cm tall. Leaf sheaths and usually the blades densely pubescent. Panicle mostly 8-12 cm long, the branches drooping.

Native annual or weak perennial, infrequent in our area and known only from a few localities in southern Texas and northern Mexico. Growing mostly in the protection of shrubs, this grass may be fairly abundant and still be relatively inconspicuous. On the Welder Foundation it grows on sandy loam soils and flowers early in the spring.

Fig. 33. *Bromus wildenowii*. Plant, spikelet and floret.

*2. BROMUS WILLDENOWII Kunth. Rescuegrass (Fig. 33). Culms usually in small clumps, rather thick and succulent, mostly 25 to 80 cm tall. Sheaths glabrous or pubescent, closed nearly to the apex. Inflorescence 6-20 cm long, with few to numerous large flattened spikelets.

An introduced annual (in our area) that is locally abundant during the cooler months in areas of disturbed soil. Rescuegrass, native to South America, was widely known in the world as *Bromus unioloides* H.B.K. until Hitchcock took up the name *Bromus catharticus* Vahl. The latter name now is recognized as a *"nomen confusum"* and invalid. On the basis of recent investigations, Raven (1960) has concluded that two distinct species exist in the "rescuegrass complex" of South America, *B. unioloides* and *B. willdenowii* Kunth, and that the common rescuegrass of southern U. S. is referrable to the latter.

11. BUCHLOE

A genus of one species, this widely distributed in western United States and northern Mexico and a dominant of the "short grass prairie" of the Great Plains area of western United States.

*1. BUCHLOE DACTYLOIDES (Nutt.) Engelm. Buffalograss (Fig. 34). Tufted perennial with widely spreading stolons and erect culms usually not over 15 or 20 cm tall. Ligule a fringe of hairs about 1 mm long. Blades short, mostly 2 mm or less broad, with a few long hairs near the base. Buffalograss is readily recognized by its low habit, slender-creeping glabrous stolons and dioecious habit. Occasionally it grows with the vegetatively similar *Hilaria belangeri* from which it may be distinguished by the inflorescence characters and by the lack of hairy nodes on the stolons, characteristic of the latter. A warm-season native perennial, buffalograss is the dominant grass on most of the upland sites of our area. It has been shown to comprise 30 to 40 percent of the total herbaceous vegetation on many of the clay soils of the Victoria series. It is less abundant on loams and virtually absent from sandy loam and sandy sites. Buffalograss is rated as being only fair as a forage plant but has the additional value of providing a good sod cover.

12. CENCHRUS Sandbur

A genus of some 20 species, these in the warmer parts of both hemispheres but mostly in the Americas. In *Cenchrus* the inflorescence is a spike-like panicle with the spikelets borne in deciduous fascicles (burs). The fascicles are comprised of usually 2-4 spikelets subtended or surrounded by a dense ring of bristles, a series of flattened spines, or a combination of both. As in the genus *Setaria*, the bristles represent reduced sterile inflorescence branches and the spines quite apparently are still more highly modified branch axes. A monographic treatment of the genus *Cenchrus* has been recently presented (DeLisle, 1963).

KEY TO THE SPECIES

Spines of burs not broad and flattened at base; plants perennial
  Spines conspicuously ciliate-pubescent   *C. ciliaris*
  Spines retrorsely scabrous   *C. myosuroides*
Spines of burs with broad, flattened bases; plants annual or weakly perennial
  Burs, excluding bristles, 5-7 mm wide, with a ring of slender bristles at the base; annual   *C. echinatus*
  Burs, excluding the bristles, 3.5 mm or less wide, without slender bristles at the base; weak perennial but flowering the first year and often appearing annual   *C. incertus*

*1. CENCHRUS CILIARIS L. *(Pennisetum ciliare* (L.) Link) Buffelgrass (Fig. 35). Introduced warm-season bunchgrass, with culms 30-90 cm tall, broad flat blades, and densely flowered purplish inflorescences. Buffelgrass is well established along road and railroad right of ways throughout much of South Texas where it has been used extensively in pasture seedings and seeding following rootplowing of mesquite-infested range areas. This grass is frequent in the Coastal Bend area, both in stands persisting in pastures and as a weed of roadsides and waste places. It is rated only fair as a forage grass.

2. CENCHRUS ECHINATUS L. Southern sandbur (Fig. 36). Native warm-season annual, occasional in sand and sand-shell mixture along the coast.

Fig. 34. *Buchloe dactyloides*. Staminate plant (a), and male spikelet with glumes separated from the floret (b), and pistillate plant (c), with inflorescence (d), female spikelet (e) and spikelet cluster or "bur" (f).

Fig. 35. *Cenchrus ciliare*. Plant, spikelet cluster (bur), spikelet.

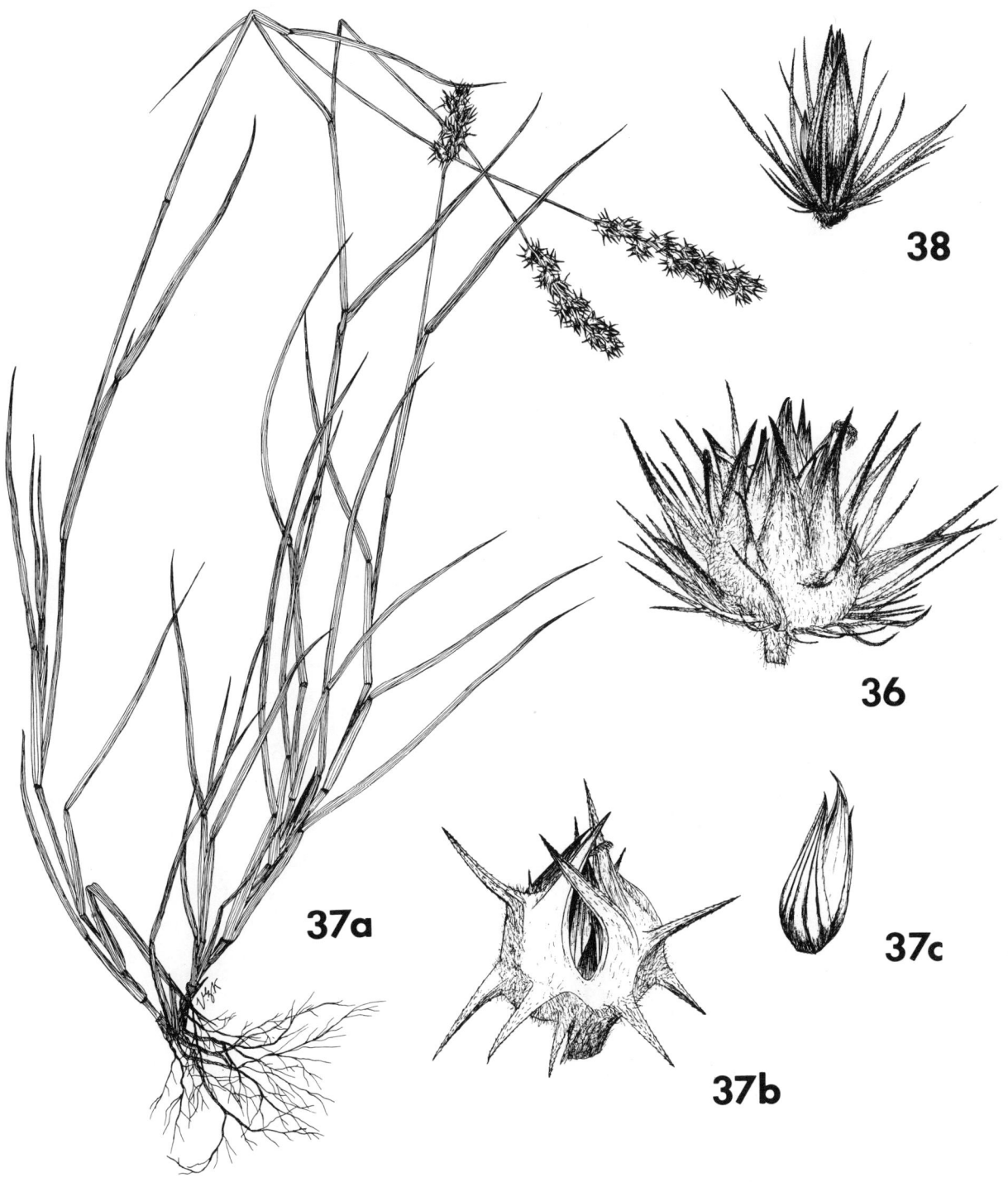

Fig. 36. *Cenchrus echinatus*. Flower cluster (bur).
Fig. 37. *Cenchrus incertus*. Plant (a), bur (b), and spikelet (c).
Fig. 38. *Cenchrus myosuroides*. Flower cluster (bur).

*3. **CENCHRUS INCERTUS** M. A. Curtis. Coast sandbur (Fig. 37). Native warm-season perennial but appearing as an annual the first year. Wide-spread and "pestiferous" throughout the area, most abundant on disturbed sandy or sandy loam soils.

NOTE. Plants with small burs, collected on the Welder Refuge, have been referred to *C. parviceps* Shinners. This taxon, however, is not recognized as distinct from *C. incertus* in the recent monographic study of DeLisle (1963).

*4. **CENCHRUS MYOSUROIDES** H.B.K. Big sandbur (Fig. 38). Native warm-season perennial with stiff, stout culms 70-130 cm or more tall, usually in large dense clumps. Occasional on several sites on our area, this grass appears to have considerable potential as a forage plant.

13. CHLORIS Windmillgrass

Inflorescence of few to several unilateral spicate branches, these verticelled or aggregated or the upper portion of the inflorescence axis. Spikelets with a single fertile floret and typically 1 rudiment above. Characteristically the culm bases and stolons are flattened and the leaf sheaths keeled.

Species about 60, distributed in tropical and subtropical regions of the world and growing as warm-season plants in our area. All but one of our species are classed as perennials but most appear to grow as annuals when occurring as pioneers on disturbed soils.

KEY TO THE SPECIES

Lemmas obtuse or mucronate, awnless, dark; glumes with a short stout awn from a broad, notched apex   *C. petraea*
Lemmas awned; glumes acute and awnless or narrowing to an acuminate (or slightly notched) awned apex
  Spikelets with 2 or more rudiments above the fertile floret
    Midnerve and lateral nerves of lemma of fertile floret ciliate with long, spreading hairs   *C. ciliata*
    Midnerve of lemma of fertile floret glabrous, the lateral nerves appressed-hirsute   *C. gayana*
  Spikelets with a single rudiment above the fertile floret
    Lemmas conspicuously ciliate with hairs 1 mm or more long
      Plants annual; lemma long-ciliate on the lateral nerves near the apex   *C. virgata*
      Plants perennial; lateral nerves of the lemma more or less uniformly ciliate
        Inflorescence branches mostly 10-15 cm long, flexuous; hairs of lemma exceeding the spikelet; awn of lemma about 3 mm long   *C. polydactyla*
        Inflorescence branches mostly 5-7 cm long, straight; hairs of lemma about equalling the spikelet; lemma awn less than 3 mm long   *C. ciliata*
    Lemmas finely puberulent or ciliate, the hairs less than 1 mm long
      Rudiment large, with a truncate apex 0.6-1.5 mm broad
        Inflorescence branches mostly 7-12 cm long; awn of lemma usually 3-8 mm long   *C. verticillata*
        Inflorescence branches mostly 3-7 cm long; awn of lemma 1-3 mm long
          Awn of lemma about 1 mm long; rudiment about 1.5 mm broad at apex   *C. cucullata*
          Awn of lemma 2-3 mm long; rudiment 0.6-1.0 mm broad at apex
            Rudiment about 0.6 mm broad at apex   *C. subdolichostachya*
            Rudiment about 1.0 mm broad at apex   *C. latisquamea*
      Rudiment small and narrow, less than 0.6 mm broad at the apex; spikelets widely spaced and closely appressed to the branches
        Fertile lemma about 2.5 mm long; inflorescence branches rarely as much as 10 cm long, spikelet-bearing to the base   *C. andropogonoides*
        Fertile lemma 4-7 mm long; inflorescence branches mostly more than 10 cm long
          Inflorescence branches in one or two verticels, bare of spikelets on the lower portion   *C. texensis*
          Inflorescence branches more or less scattered, bearing spikelets to the base   *C. chloridea*

Fig. 39. *Chloris andropogonoides*. Inflorescence and spikelet.

*1. **CHLORIS ANDROPOGONOIDES** Fourn. SLIMSPIKE WINDMILLGRASS (Fig. 39). Plants tufted, spreading by stout stolons. Culms mostly 10-30 cm tall, flattened at the base. Lower sheaths strongly keeled, with white membranous margins. Ligule a fringe of hairs less than 0.5 mm long. Bases of inflorescence branches with swollen, hirsute pulvini. Spikelet 2-3 mm long, the lemma of the fertile floret about 5 mm long. Native perennial, occasional to frequent on sandy loams, loams and clay loams. Usually associated with buffalograss. Of poor grazing value.

*2. **CHLORIS CHLORIDEA** (Presl.) Hitchc. BURYSEED CHLORIS (Fig. 40). Native perennial with culms 60-100 cm tall, long flat blades and spicate inflorence branches mostly 8-15 cm long. Large cleistogamous spikelets are borne on slender underground branches. This grass is infrequent in our area and of little or no forage significance.

47

Fig. 40. *Chloris chloridea*. Base of plant showing cleistogenes on rhizomes, leafy culm with inflorescence, aerial spikelet (left) and caryopsis of aerial spikelet (left center) and large caryopsis of subterrainian spikelet (center).

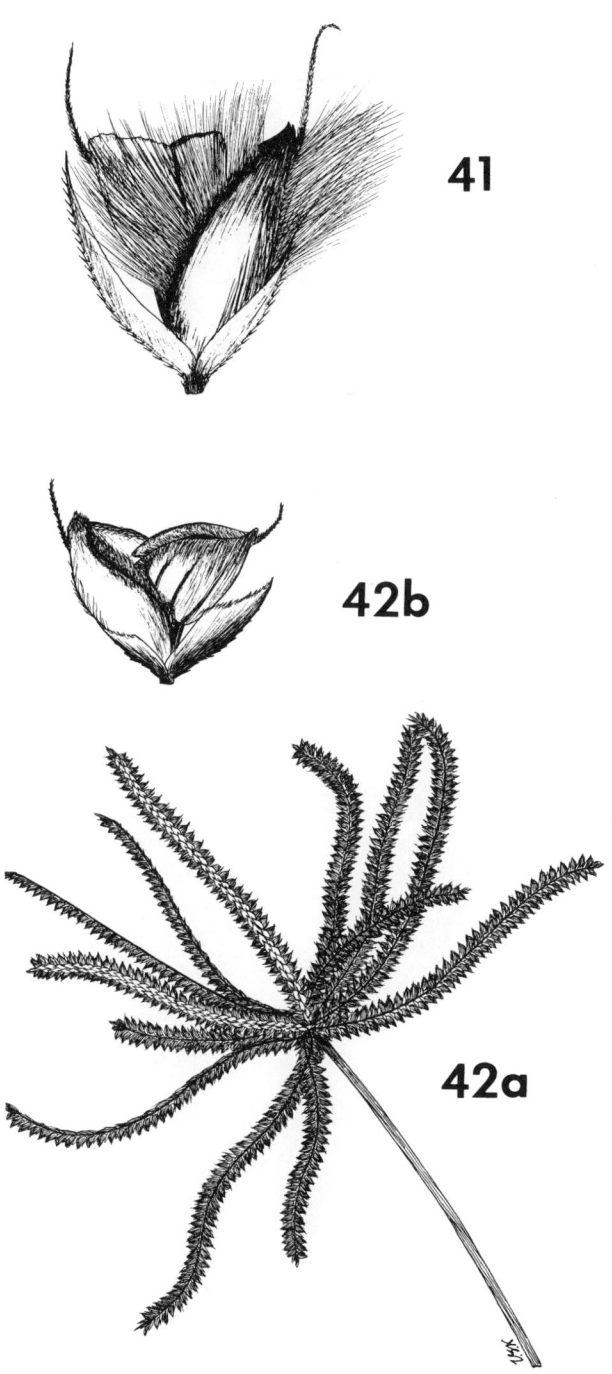

Fig. 41. *Chloris ciliata*. Spikelet.
Fig. 42 a-b. *Chloris cucullata*. Inflorescence and spikelet.

*3. **CHLORIS CILIATA** Swartz. Fringed chloris (Fig. 41). Native perennial, occasional on well-drained sites. Fringed chloris usually grows on soils with slightly higher clay content than those that support *Chloris cucullata* and *C. latisquamea*.

*4. **CHLORIS CUCULLATA** Bisch. Hooded windmillgrass (Fig. 42). Native perennial, occasional to frequent on sandy and sandy loam soils, especially those in a disturbed condition. Typically the inflorescence of *C. cucullata* has relatively thick, short branches and dark, almost black, spikelets at maturity.

*5. **CHLORIS GAYANA** Kunth. Rhodesgrass (Fig. 43). Introduced perennial with moderately tall erect culms and stout stolons. Rhodesgrass is a vigorous grower and good forage grass. It has been used extensively in pasture reseeding and now is rather frequent as a roadside grass throughout our area. It is, however, highly susceptable to scale insects, a factor that has restricted its use in southern Texas where otherwise it seems well adapted.

*6. **CHLORIS LATISQUAMEA** Nash. Nash windmillgrass (Fig. 44). Ligule a fringed membrane 1 mm or more long. Inflorescence branches with hirsute reddish pulvini. Native perennial, growing on sandy and sandy loam sites throughout our area, most frequently in shaded sites.

Plants referrable to this species are intermediate in characteristics between *C. cucullata* and *C. verticillata* and cytological studies indicate that the taxon consists largely if not entirely of hybrids and hybrid derivatives of these two species.

*7. **CHLORIS PETRAEA** Swartz. Stiffleaf chloris (Fig. 45). Native perennial, occasional on sandy and sandy loam soils, usually in moist situations near permanent brackish water. Of little or no forage significance.

8. **CHLORIS POLYDACTYLA** (L.) Swartz. Manyspiked chloris (Fig. 46). Introduced perennial. Occasional as a roadside grass in our area.

*9. **CHLORIS SUBDOLICHOSTACHYA** C. Muell. Shortspike windmillgrass (Fig. 47). Infrequent native perennial. Plants referrable to this species, similar to those of *C. latisquamea*, may all be hybrids of hybrid derivatives of *C. cucullata* and *C. verticillata*.

*10. **CHLORIS TEXENSIS** Nash. Texas windmillgrass. (Fig. 48). Native perennial, not uncommon on disturbed sites such as roadways and ditches, especially on sandy and sandy loam soils. Of little forage significance.

Fig. 43. *Chloris gayana*. Plant and spikelet.

Fig. 44. *Chloris latisquamea*. Spikelet.
Fig. 45 a-b. *Chloris petraea*. Inflorescence and spikelet.

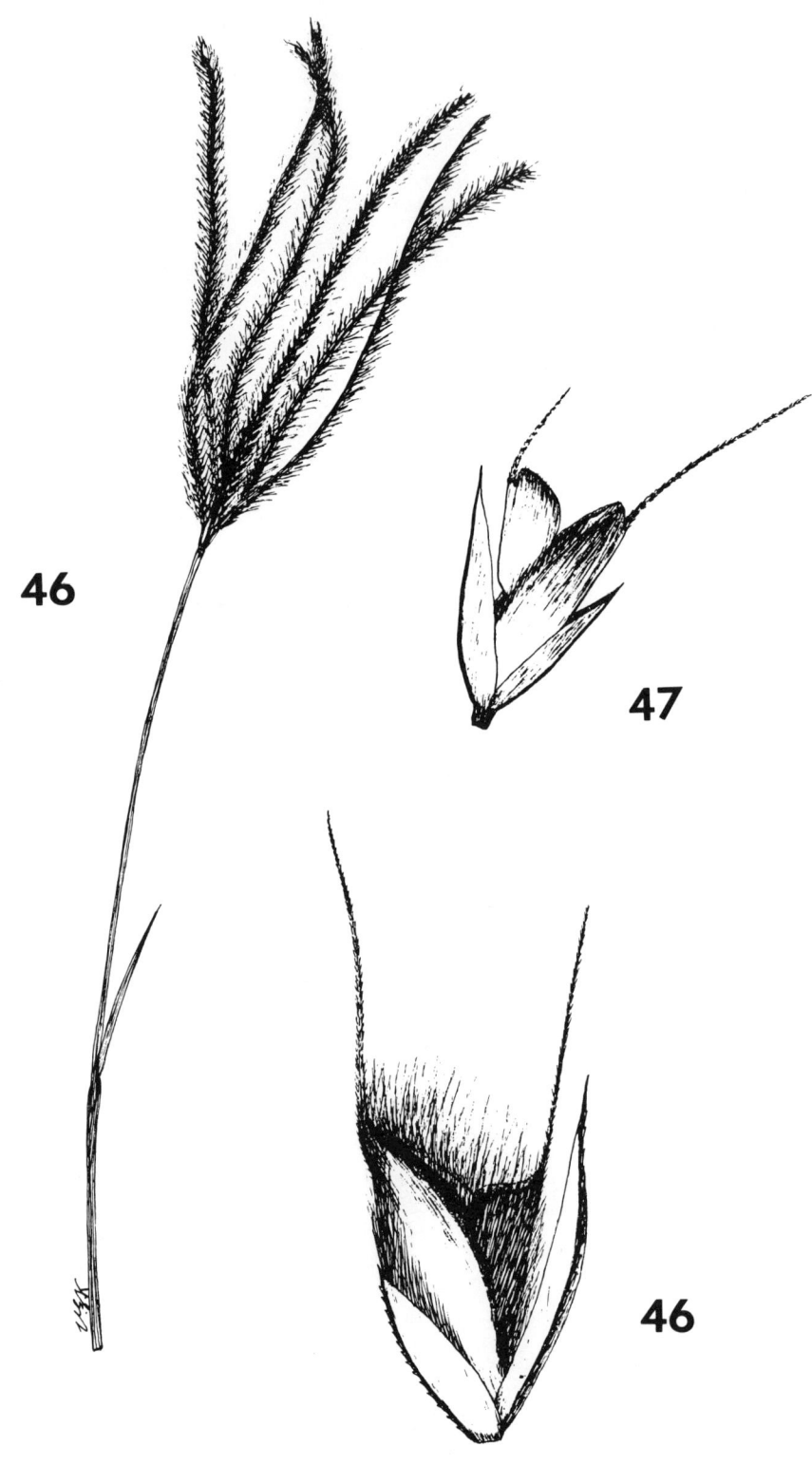

Fig. 46. *Chloris polydactyla*. Inflorescence and spikelet.
Fig. 47. *Chloris subdolichostachya*. Spikelet.

Fig. 48. *Chloris texensis*. Inflorescence and spikelet.

Fig. 49. *Chloris verticillata*. Plant and spikelet.

Fig. 50. *Chloris virgata*. Plant and spikelet with glumes separated.

*11. **CHLORIS VERTICILLATA** Nutt. TUMBLE WINDMILLGRASS. (Fig. 49). Native perennial, frequent throughout the area, especially on disturbed soils or in heavily grazed areas. Similar to the closely related *C. cucullata*, *C. verticillata* produces relatively little forage and has only poor to fair grazing value.

12. **CHLORIS VIRGATA** Swartz. SHOWY CHLORIS (Fig. 50). Native annual, growing as a common weed in many areas of Texas but infrequent in the Coastal Bend.

14. CORTADERIA

Dioecious grasses with several-flowered spikelets in large silvery panicles. Glumes longer than the lower florets. Lemmas of the pistillate florets bearing long silky hairs, the lemmas of the staminate florets glabrous. A genus of about 5 species, none native to the United States.

*1. **CORTADERIA SELLOANA** (Schult.) Aschers and Graebn. PAMPASGRASS. Introduced lawn ornamental, relatively hardy but infrequent outside of cultivation.

Fig. 51. *Cynodon dactylon*. Plant inflorescence and spikelet.

Fig. 52. *Dactyloctenium aegyptium*. Inflorescence and spikelet.

15. CYNODON

Stoloniferous and rhizomatous perennials with inflorescences of few to several slender spicate branches digitately arranged at the culm apex. Species about 10, mostly African and Australian. One species, *C. dactylon,* widely distributed in the warmer regions of both hemispheres.

*1. CYNODON DACTYLON (L.) Pers. BERMUDAGRASS (Fig. 51). Introduced warm-season perennial, locally abundant in our area. Bermudagrass is best adapted to low moist sites but is relatively drought-resistant. It is quite highly salt- and alkali-tolerant. The improved hybrid strain "coastal bermuda" has been widely established as a pasture grass in eastern Texas and along the coast. This strain is larger and coarser than "common bermuda" and due to its hybrid nature produces few inflorescences and does not set viable seed. Both common and Coastal Bermuda are good forage grasses, especially in fertilized pastures.

16. DACTYLOCTENIUM

A genus of about five species, these native to the warmer regions of the Eastern Hemisphere.

*1. DACTYLOCTENIUM AEGYPTIUM (L.) Richt. DURBAN CROWFOOT (Fig. 52). Adventive warm-season annual. Inflorescence with 2 to several short, thick, closely flowered, digitately arranged branches. Axis of inflorescence branch projecting beyond the last spikelet. Spikelets 2-5 flowered, laterally flattened. Lemmas 3-nerved, the lateral nerves indistinct. This grass is an occasional weed of ditches, roadsides and other disturbed sites.

17. DIGITARIA

Annuals and perennials, with erect or decumbent, often stoloniferous culms. Spikelets solitary or paired on slender, spicate inflorescence branches, these digitate or scattered. Spikelets lanceolate or elliptic, acuminate or narrowly acute at apex. First glume vestigial or absent, second glume equalling or shorter than the sterile lemma. Fertile lemma thin and cartilaginous, with membranous, flat margins.

A genus of about 75 species, distributed in the tropics and subtropics of the world. Including those species referred to *Trichachne* by Hitchcock, some 22 species occur in the United States, 12 in Texas. Following the monographic treatment of *Digitaria* by Henrard (1950), the grasses previously referred to *Trichachne* are included in this genus. *Trichachne* was recognized as a separate genus mainly on the presence of long silky hairs on the second glume and sterile lemma and the acute apex of the fertile lemma. These differences, however, are not consistent, and the species of the *Trichachne* group appear best treated as a subgenus or section of *Digitaria*.

KEY TO THE SPECIES

Rachis of inflorescence branch broadly winged, with wings about as wide as the body; annuals with weak, usually decumbent or trailing culms, these rooting at the lower nodes

    Sterile lemma of lower spikelet of a pair with 5 equidistant nerves, glabrous or minutely pubescent laterally; first glume of lower spikelet rounded or truncate, 0.3 mm or less long; sterile lemma of upper spikelet of a pair densely villous on the margins
D. diversiflora

    Sterile lemma of lower spikelet of a pair 5-nerved but these not equidistant, the lateral ones crowded to the margins; sterile lemma of both spikelets of a pair glabrous or variously pubescent on the lateral nerves; first glume of lowermost spikelet of a pair obtuse or acute, often more than 0.3 mm long.

        Second glume 1.6-2.7 mm long; spikelets 2.8 (occasionally 2.5) - 3.5 mm long; sterile lemma not scabrous-hispid on the lateral nerves; leaves glabrous or sparsely pubescent with pappila-based hairs.
D. adscendens

        Second glume 1.0-1.7 mm long; spikelets 2.2-3.0 (occasionally 3.2) mm long; lateral nerves of the sterile lemma scabrous-hispid; leaves rather densely covered with pappila-based hairs, the blades usually pubescent on both surfaces for their entire length
D. sanguinalis

Rachis of inflorescence branches wingless or nearly so; perennials with a hard knotty base of short, stout rhizomes
  Spikelets silky-pubescent with long silvery hairs; leaf blades 2-4 mm broad
    Inflorescence branches stiffly erect-spreading, with widely spaced spikelets; caryopsis gradually narrowing to a point   *D. patens*
    Inflorescence branches erect-appressed, closely flowered; caryopsis abruptly pointed   *D. californica*
  Spikelet glabrous or variously pubescent but not with long silvery hairs
    Mature fertile lemma dark brown or purple; second glume and sterile lemma puberulent on the nerves with capitellate hairs   *D. filiformis* var. *villosa*
    Mature fertile lemma light brown or grayish; second glume and sterile lemma glabrous or pubescent but the hairs not capitellate
      Spikelets mostly 3.6-4.2 mm long, bearing long brownish hairs; leaves glabrous or essentially so; creeping rhizomes never developed   *D. insularis*
      Spikelets less than 3.6 mm long, hairy or glabrous; leaves, at least the lowermost, usually densely villous; stout creeping rhizomes usually developed
        Spikelets 2-2.5 mm long, sparsely villous to glabrous   *D. texana*
        Spikelets 2.8-3.6 mm long, usually densely villous   *D. runyoni*

*1. DIGITARIA ADSCENDENS (H.B.K.) Henrard. Weedy warm-season annual, similar to *D. sanguinalis* in general aspect. The morphological relationships of these two species was discussed in a recent paper by Ebinger (1962). Gould (1963) has noted that *D. adscendens* is a hexaploid with $2n=54$ chromosomes while *D. sanguinalis* is tetraploid with $2n=36$ chromosomes.

Digitaria adscendens is frequent in ditches, flower gardens, fencerows and other disturbed sites throughout the Coastal Bend area. Its North American distribution for the most part is southern Virginia to southeastern Nebraska, eastern and southern Texas, and south through Mexico at low elevations. Plants of this species in our area previously have been referred to *D. sanguinalis*.

2. DIGITARIA CALIFORNICA (Benth.) Henrard. (*Trichachne californica* (Benth.) Chase). ARIZONA COTTONTOP (Fig. 53). Native warm-season tufted perennial, with a contracted panicle of silvery-pubescent spikelets. Widespread in sandy soils throughout the Southwest. Not recorded in the Coastal Bend area but to be expected.

*3. DIGITARIA DIVERSIFLORA Swallen. A recently described species (Swallen, 1963) that is very similar to *D. adscendens* in general characteristics, habitat preference and distribution. In the original description, Swallen stated the leaf blades to be 4-5 cm long and 3.5-5.0 mm broad and the inflorescence branches to be 4-8 cm long. Plants of our area tend to have larger blades and longer inflorescence branches but are typical in spikelet characters.

4. DIGITARIA FILIFORMIS (L.) Koel. var. *villosa* (Walt.) Fern. (*D. villosa* (Walt.) Pers.) SHAGGY CRABGRASS. Culms mostly 70-150 cm tall. Sheaths and blades glabrous or pubescent. Blades mostly 3-6 mm wide. Inflorescence branches usually 15-25 cm long. Spikelets 2-2.5 mm long. This tall, rather coarse perennial has been collected on the Aransas Wildlife Refuge (Aransas County).

*5. DIGITARIA INSULARIS (L.) Mez ex Ekman. (*Trichachne insularis* (L.) Nees). SOURGRASS (Fig. 54). Culms mostly in large clumps, 70-100 cm tall. Native warm season perennial, occasional in our area on sandy and sandy loam sites. This grass provides good forage in the Coastal Bend area but in tropical America, where it is widespread and abundant as a weed of disturbed sites, it reportedly is unpalatable to livestock.

*6. DIGITARIA PATENS (Swallen) Henrard. (*Trichachne patens* Swallen). TEXAS COTTONTOP (Fig. 55). Native tufted warm-season perennial, with an open panicle of widely spaced silvery-pubescent spikelets on slender branches. Occasional in our area on sandy and sandy loam soils, never abundant. A fair to good forage grass.

7. DIGITARIA RUNYONI Hitchc. DUNE CRABGRASS (Fig. 56). Culms mostly 40-75 cm tall, from firm, many-noded rhizomes. Sheaths and blades, at least the lower, densely villous-pubescent. Native warm-season perennial, known only from sandy coastal soils and dunes of the lower Texas gulf region.

Fig. 53. *Digitaria californica*. Plant and spikelet.

8. **DIGITARIA SANGUINALIS** (L.) Scop. HAIRY CRABGRASS (Fig. 57). Weedy introduced annual of disturbed soils. This species has its major distribution in North America from southeastern Canada to Virginia, Kentucky, and North Texas westward to the Pacific Coast and at the higher elevations in Mexico. Most plants of southern United States previously referred to this species are now included in *D. adscendens* and *D. diversiflora*. *Digitaria sanguinalis* may be present in the Coastal Bend region but has not yet been recorded here.

9. **DIGITARIA TEXANA** Hitchc. TEXAS CRABGRASS (Fig. 58). Native warm-season perennial, similar to *D. runyoni* but typically with smaller spikelets and less pubescent sheaths and blades. *Digitaria runyoni* and *D. texana* both are known only from the sandy coastal area of the middle and lower Texas Gulf region. Hitchcock's Manual reports the habitat for *D. runyoni* as "sand dunes and sandy prairies along the coast" and for *D. texana* as "sandy oak woods or sandy prairie." Further investigation may show these two to be only varietally distinct.

Fig. 54 a-b. *Digitaria insularis*. Inflorescence and spikelet.

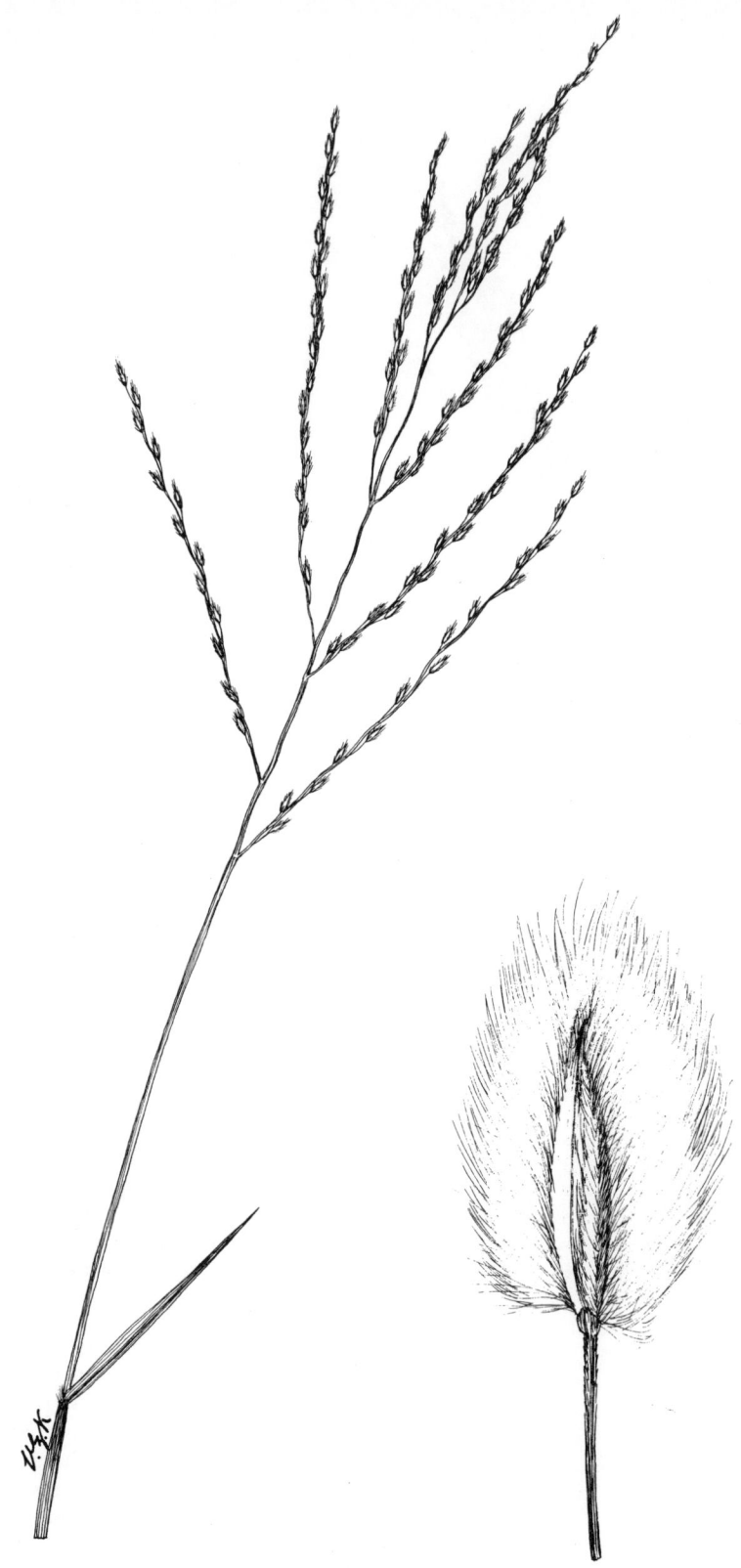

Fig. 55. *Digitaria patens*. Inflorescence and spikelet.

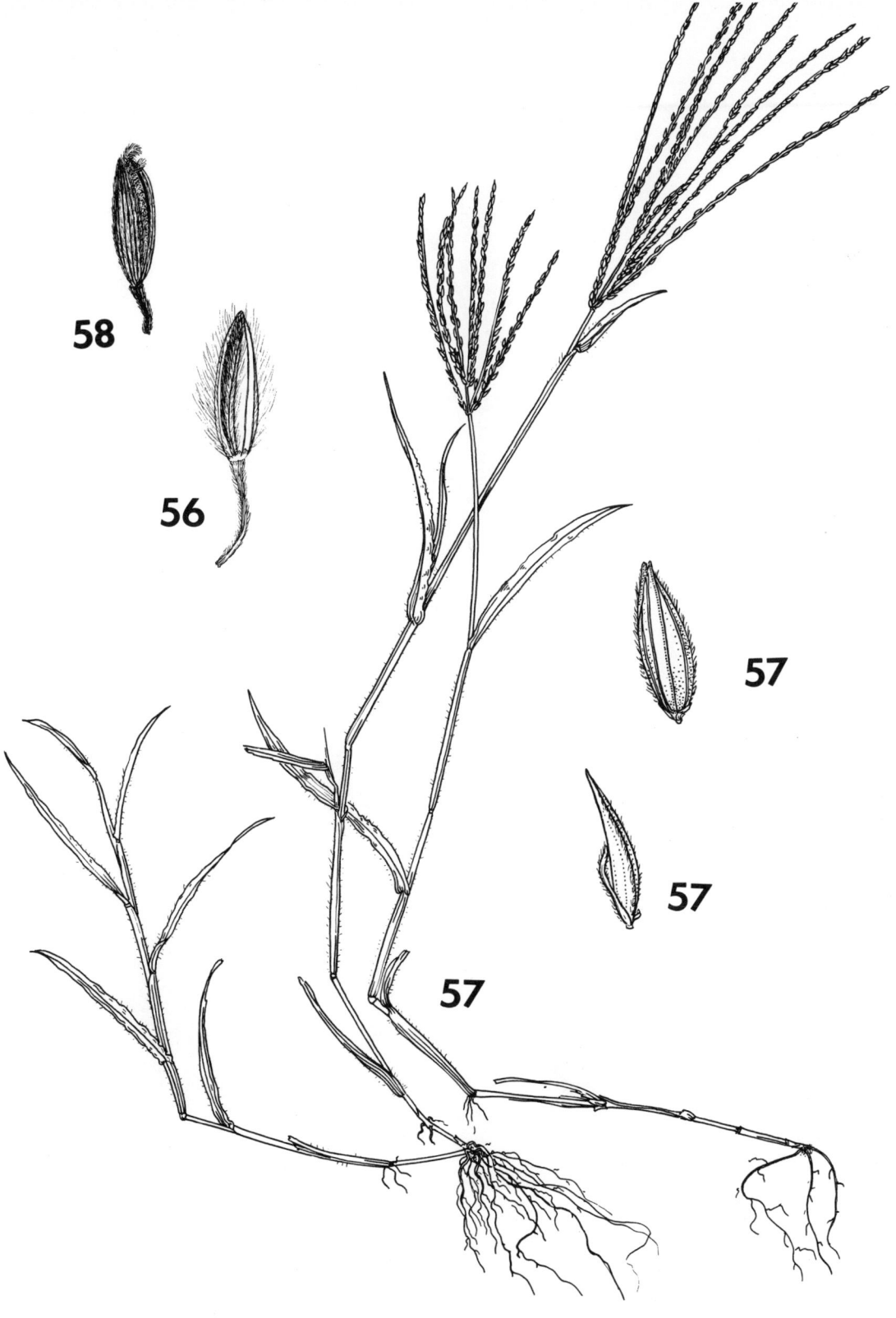

Fig. 56. *Digitaria runyoni*. Spikelet.
Fig. 57. *Digitaria sanguinalis*. Plant and 2 views of spikelet.
Fig. 58. *Digitaria texana*. Spikelet.

Fig. 59. *Distichlis spicata*. Plant with pistillate inflorescence and separate staminate inflorescence.

18. DISTICHLIS Saltgrass

Low dioecious (rarely monoecious) perennials with stout rhizomes, firm glabrous culms and leaves, contracted panicles or spikelike racemes and relatively large, flattened, awnless, several-flowered spikelets.

Species about six, mostly in North and South America, generally adapted to salt and alkaline marshes and tidelands.

*1. DISTICHLIS SPICATA L. Greene, var. *spicata*. SEASHORE SALTGRASS (Fig. 59). Locally abundant in the Coastal Bend area in highly saline and alkaline sites, often growing in dense stands. Seashore saltgrass is a good forage plant in salty sites.

19. ECHINOCHLOA

A genus of about 15 species, closely related to *Panicum* and similarly distributed in the warmer parts of the world. Our species are warm-season plants that grow in moist habitats and are weedy in general aspect.

KEY TO THE SPECIES

Ligule a line of hairs; perennial   *E. polystachya*
Ligule absent; annuals
    Panicle branches 1-2 (occasionally 3) cm long, simple; spikelets in 2-4 rather regular rows; blades usually 6 mm or less broad; second glume and sterile lemma acute to acuminate, usually somewhat papillose-hispid   *E. colonum*
    Panicle branches commonly 2.5-6 cm long, usually with short spur branches; spikelets fascicled, not in regular rows; blades often much more than 6 mm broad; second glume and sterile lemma acuminate to awned.
    Sheaths, at least the lower, hispid or scabrous; panicle dense, the spikelets long-awned   *E. walteri*
    Sheaths glabrous, spikelets awned or awnless but panicle not a dense mass of long-awned spikelets
      Panicles nodding, lax; spikelets inconspicuously hispid   *E. crus-pavonis*
      Panicle usually stiffly erect (heavy panicles somewhat nodding); spikelets conspicuously hispid   *E. crusgalli*

*1. ECHINOCHLOA COLONUM (L.) Link. JUNGLERICE (Fig. 60). Leaves without ligule or auricles, commonly glabrous at the junction of the sheath and blade. Culms succulent, usually decumbent and spreading. Blades flat, moderately broad, usually with transverse purple bands or markings. Introduced annual, a common weed of flower beds, ditches and similar moist, disturbed habitats.

*2. ECHINOCHLOA CRUSGALLI (L.) Beauv. BARNYARDGRASS (Fig. 61). Introduced annual, for the most part a rather large, succulent plant with glabrous herbage and a contracted, densely flowered inflorescence. Ligule absent. Blades flat, often 5-12 mm broad but narrower on depauperate plants. Barnyardgrass is locally abundant on poorly drained sites throughout the Coastal Bend area. It is of little significance for livestock forage, but the abundance of large caryopsis produced provide excellent wildlife food.

Echinochloa crusgalli is distributed throughout the warmer parts of the world. Many varieties have been recognized in this polymorphic species. The taxonomy of this and related taxa, however, need further study before subspecific categories can be clearly defined. Most of the plants of the Coastal Bend are referrable to var. *macera* (Wieg.) Shinners. The var. *frumentacea* (Roxb.) W. F. Wight, commonly known as Japanese millet, also is listed by Jones et al. (1961) for our area.

*3. ECHINOCHLOA CRUS-PAVONIS (H.B.K.) Schult. GULF COCKSPUR. Large coarse native annual, with bristly nodding panicle. Occasional along swamps and swales, often in shallow water during rainy periods.

4. ECHINOCHLOA POLYSTACHYA (H. B.K.) Hitchc. Coarse native perennial with culms 1 to 2 meters tall. Infrequent in our area, occasional in swampy sites.

5. ECHINOCHLOA WALTERI (Pursh) Heller. COAST COCKSPUR (Fig. 62). Coarse native annual, with culms 1 to 2 meters tall. Inflorescence dense and bristly, the spikelet awns typically 1 to 2.5 cm long. Without definite record in our area but to be expected.

Fig. 60. *Echinochloa colonum*. Plant and spikelet.

Fig. 61 a-b. *Echinochloa crusgallii*. Inflorescence and spikelet.

Fig. 62. *Echinochloa walteri.* Inflorescence.

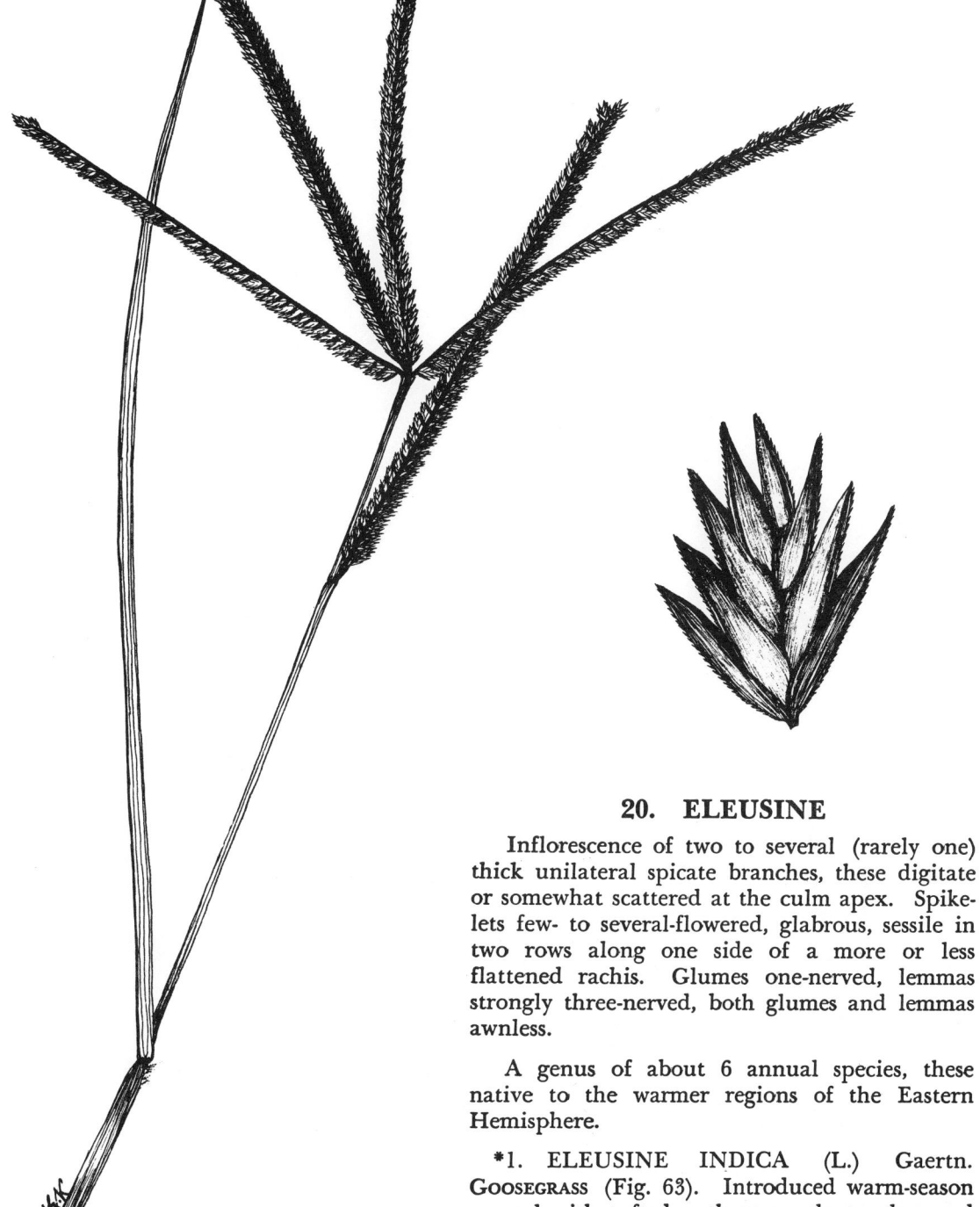

20. ELEUSINE

Inflorescence of two to several (rarely one) thick unilateral spicate branches, these digitate or somewhat scattered at the culm apex. Spikelets few- to several-flowered, glabrous, sessile in two rows along one side of a more or less flattened rachis. Glumes one-nerved, lemmas strongly three-nerved, both glumes and lemmas awnless.

A genus of about 6 annual species, these native to the warmer regions of the Eastern Hemisphere.

*1. ELEUSINE INDICA (L.) Gaertn. GOOSEGRASS (Fig. 63). Introduced warm-season annual with tufted, rather succulent culms and coarse flat blades. A common and widespread weed of roadsides, gardens and other disturbed sites in Texas. In our area goosegrass is infrequent.

Fig. 63. *Eleusine indica.* Inflorescence and spikelet.

21. ELYMUS Wildrye

As commonly delimited, a genus of about 45 species, with distribution mostly in the temperate and cold regions of the Northern Hemisphere. In Texas these grasses grow as cool-season plants. Characteristically the inflorescence is a spike with 2-4 spikelets per node, and 2-several florets per spikelets.

Fig. 64 a-b. *Elymus canadensis*. Plant and spikelet with glumes separated from the floret.
Fig. 65. *Elymus virginicus*. Inflorescence.

KEY TO THE SPECIES

Base of glumes hard, terete, bowed outward; awn of lemma typically short and straight
E. virginicus

Base of glumes not hard, terete and bowed out; awn of lemma usually relatively long and outward curving
E. canadensis

*1. **ELYMUS CANADENSIS** L. CANADA WILDRYE (Fig. 64). Native perennial with broad blades and slender, tall, rather succulent culms in small clumps. Three varieties of Canada wildrye are recognized in Hitchcock's "Manual of the Grasses of the United States" (1950) but none appear especially significant. This and the next species, *E. virginicus*, are locally frequent in early spring on open shaded areas of sandy and sandy loam sites. Both are highly palatable to livestock and, being weak perennials, they are eliminated from heavily grazed areas.

*2. **ELYMUS VIRGINICUS** L. VIRGINIA WILDRYE (Fig. 65). Similar to *E. canadensis* in general aspect and characteristics and also with numerous named varieties. The plants of our area probably are all referable to the var. *glabriflorus* (Vasey) Bush. Hybrid swarms between *E. canadensis* and *E. virginicus* are not infreqeunt.

22. ELYONURUS Balsamscale

A small genus of perennials with solitary, spikelike racemes. These grasses are distributed in the tropics and subtropics of both hemispheres. Only two species occur in the United States, these in a relatively narrow strip from Florida to Arizona.

*1. **ELYONURUS TRIPSACOIDES** Humb. and Bonpl. PAN AMERICAN BALSAMSCALE (Fig. 66). Native warm-season perennial, usually developing short rhizomes. Occasional to locally abundant on sandy and sandy loam sites. Of fair to poor forage value.

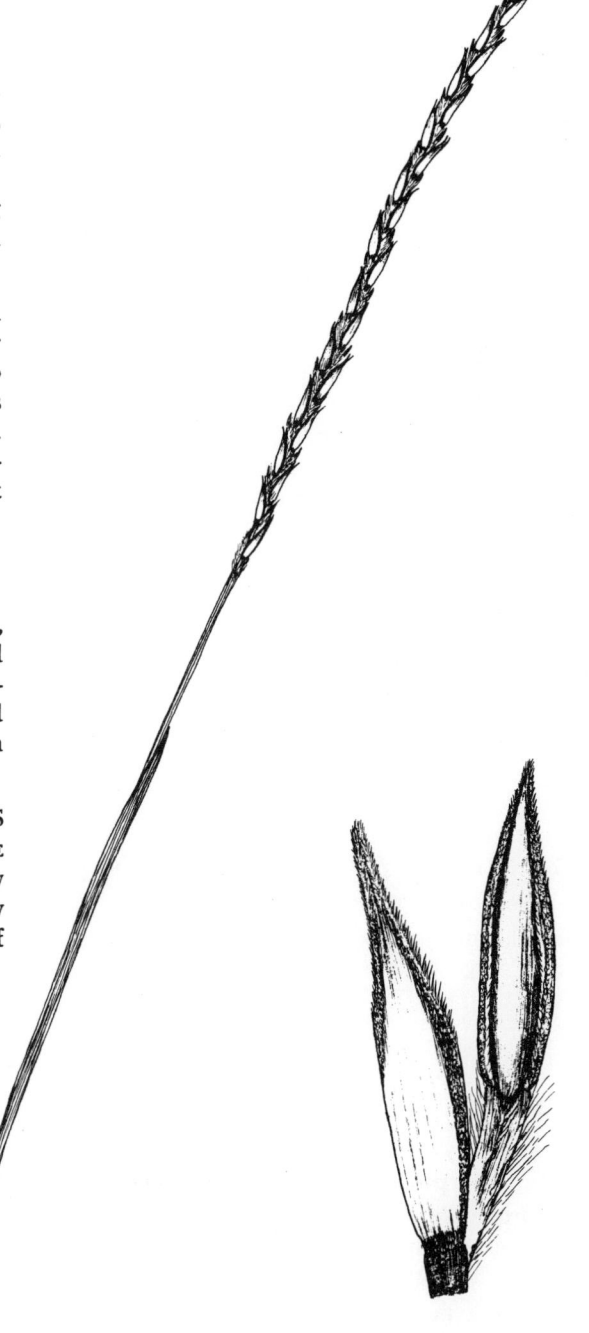

Fig. 66. *Elyonurus tripsacoides*. Inflorescence and spikelet pair.

23. ERAGROSTIS Lovegrass

Annuals and perennials, mostly with small spikelets in open, many-flowered panicles; lemmas three-nerved, awnless. Species about 250, in temperate and tropical regions of the world. Several forage species have been introduced into this country from the Mediterranean region and South Africa.

KEY TO THE SPECIES

Main inflorescence axis with glandular blotches or spots below the branches, or pedicel of spikelet bearing a glandular band or spot above the middle, or lemmas with minute, elevated glands on the keels
  Plants annual; culms usually decumbent or spreading at base
    Spikelets without glands on the keels of the lemmas; spikelets mostly 1-2 mm broad
        E. barrelieri
    Spikelets with glands on the keels of the lemmas; spikelets mostly 2-3 mm broad
        E. megastachya
  Plants perennial; culms stiffly erect; pedicel bearing a glandular band or spot above the middle
        E. swalleni
Main inflorescence axis without glandular areas, lemmas without glands on the keels
  Plants mat-forming, with spreading, stoloniferous culms; annual   (See *Neeragrostis*)
  Plants not mat-forming, with erect, non-stoloniferous culms
    Spikelets sessile or subsessile, the pedicels of the lateral spikelets 1 mm or less long
      Inflorescence generally 6-15 cm long, with branches rarely more than 8 cm long; spikelets mostly 2.5-5 mm broad, borne in irregular clusters   *E. oxylepis*
      Inflorescence generally 20-40 cm long and with at least some branches 8-15 cm or more long; spikelets 3 mm or less broad, uniformly distributed along the inflorescence branches
        Lemmas 3-4 mm long; primary panicle branches unbranched or with 1 or 2 branches near the base; spikelets widely spread, seldom overlapping   *E. sessilispica*
        Lemmas 1.5-2 mm long; primary paincle branches, at least the larger, freely rebranched; spikelets often closely placed and overlapping   *E. curtipedicillata*
    Spikelets on pedicels mostly more than 1 mm long
      Plants annual   I.
      Plants perennial, with a firm, more or less "knotty" base   II.

I.

Spikelets mostly 2-3 mm long, with 2-3 (occasionally-4) florets; pedicels mostly twice or more as long as the spikelets   *E. capillaris*
Spikelets mostly 5-8 mm long, at least some with 5-13 or more florets   *E. arida*

II.

Lateral nerves of lemma conspicuous; panicle large and diffuse, usually one-half times or more the length of the culm; spikelets violet colored at maturity
  Inflorescence branches viscid; sheaths and blades glabrous or sparsely hispid; blades 1-4 (rarely —5) mm broad; inflorescence without long, slender, rigid secondary branches; spikelets purple but not rosy-tinged   *E. silveana*
  Inflorescense branches not viscid; sheaths and blades, at least the lower, usually densely hispid; blades mostly 3-8 mm broad; inflorescence typically with long, slender but rigid secondary branches; spikelets typically rosy-purple at maturity   *E. spectabilis*
Lateral nerves of lemma obscure; panicle usually less than one-half as long as the culm; spikelets lead-colored   *E. lugens*

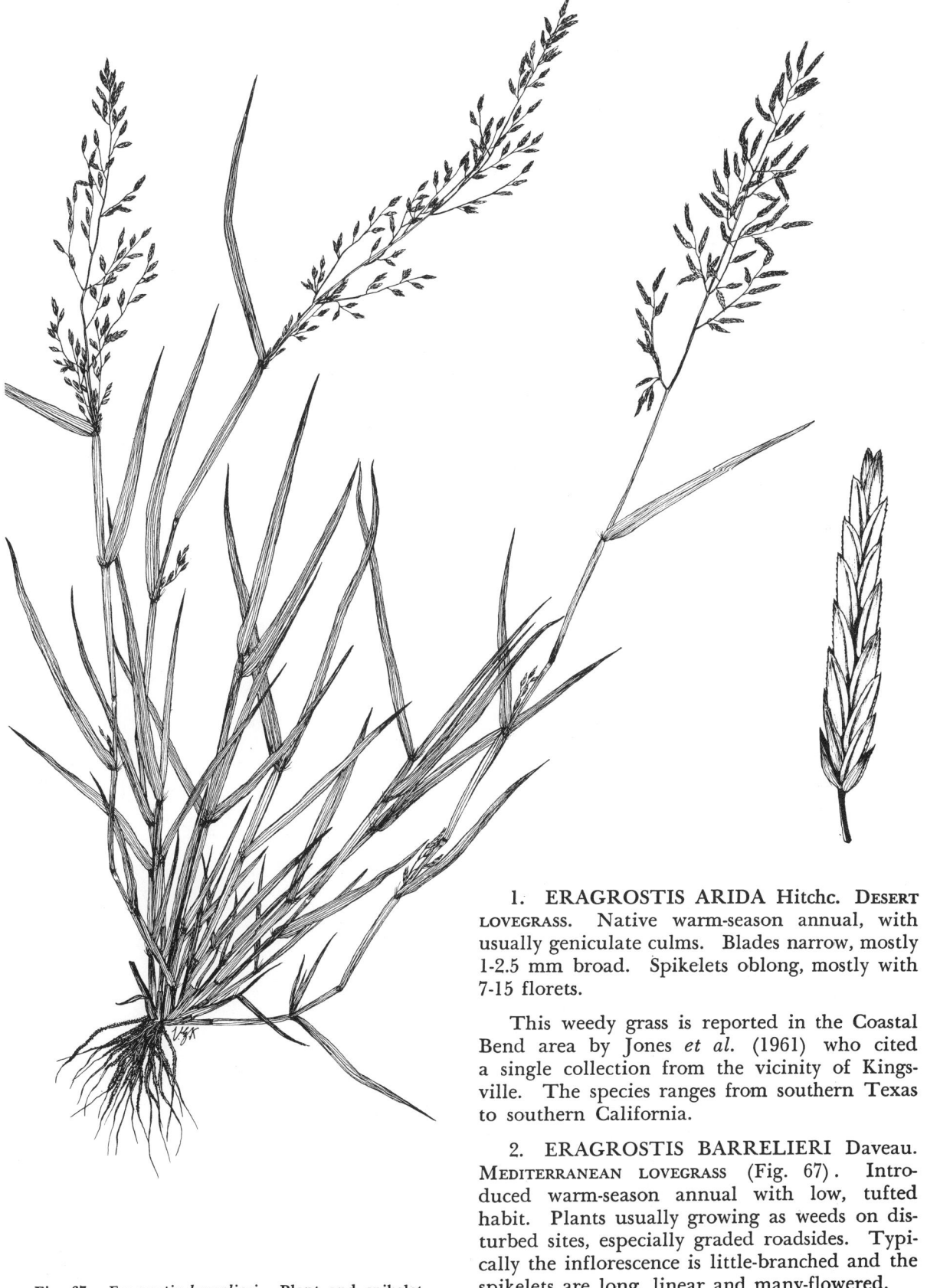

Fig. 67. *Eragrostis barrelieri*. Plant and spikelet.

1. **ERAGROSTIS ARIDA** Hitchc. DESERT LOVEGRASS. Native warm-season annual, with usually geniculate culms. Blades narrow, mostly 1-2.5 mm broad. Spikelets oblong, mostly with 7-15 florets.

This weedy grass is reported in the Coastal Bend area by Jones *et al.* (1961) who cited a single collection from the vicinity of Kingsville. The species ranges from southern Texas to southern California.

2. **ERAGROSTIS BARRELIERI** Daveau. MEDITERRANEAN LOVEGRASS (Fig. 67). Introduced warm-season annual with low, tufted habit. Plants usually growing as weeds on disturbed sites, especially graded roadsides. Typically the inflorescence is little-branched and the spikelets are long, linear and many-flowered.

3. ERAGROSTIS CAPILLARIS (L.) Nees. LACEGRASS (Fig. 68). Native annual, basically a warm-season plant but in our area one of the first grasses to flower in the spring.

Plants of this tufted annual frequently are confused with small, early-flowering plants of *E. lugens*.

4. ERAGROSTIS CURTIPEDICILLATA Buckl. GUMMY LOVEGRASS (Fig. 69). Native warm season perennial. Occasional in tight sandy clay and sandy loam soils. Of poor grazing value.

Fig. 68. *Eragrostis capillaris*. Spikelet and pedicel.
Fig. 69. *Eragrostis curtipedicillata*. Inflorescence and spikelet

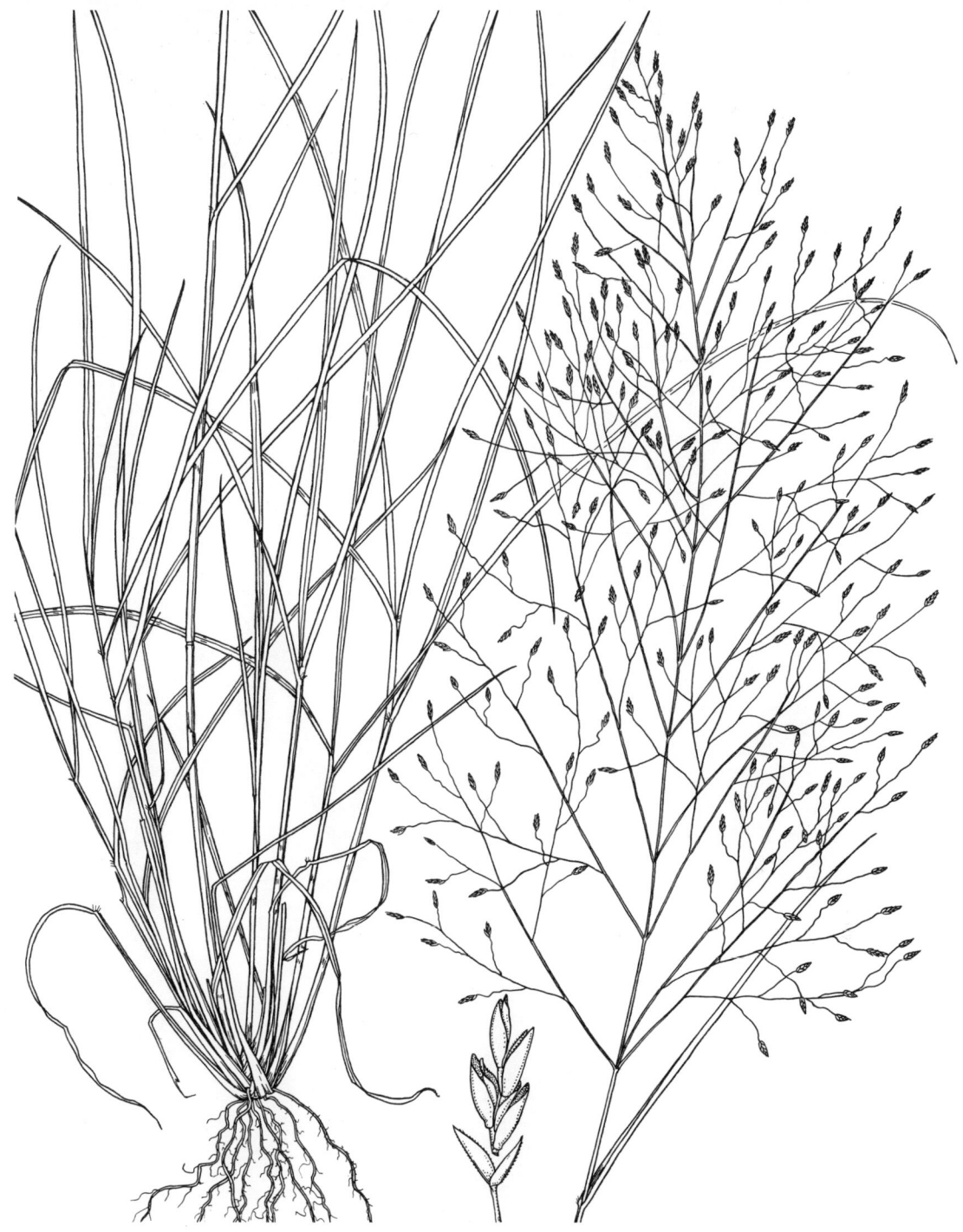

Fig. 70. *Eragrostis lugens.* Plant, with enlarged spikelet.

*5. ERAGROSTIS LUGENS Nees. Mourning Lovegrass (Fig. 70). Native perennial bunchgrass with large, open, many-flowered inflorescences. Spikelets with 3-7 florets, lead-colored. Flowering as early as January and almost continuously throughout the year, mourning lovegrass is frequent on many sites throughout our area. It is best adapted to sandy loam soils. Although of common occurrence, this grass is rated only fair in respect to grazing value. Grasses of the Texas Coastal Bend previously identified as *E. intermedia* Hitchc. are herein referred to *E. lugens.*

6. **ERAGROSTIS MEGASTACHYA** (Koel.) Link. *(Eragrostis cilianensis* of Hitchc. Man. of U. S. Grasses). STINKGRASS (Fig. 71). Low weedy annual, with relatively large, many-flowered spikelets. Lemmas minutely glandular on the keels. This Old World species has become widely established as a weed of roadsides and other disturbed sites throughout the United States. It is especially well adapted to heavy-soiled bottomlands. Jones *et al.* (1961) report it to have been collected in the Corpus Christi area by Heller in 1894.

*7. **ERAGROSTIS OXYLEPIS** (Torr. Torr. (Including *E. beyrichii* J. G. Smith). RED LOVEGRASS (Fig. 72). Warm-season perennial, highly variable in size, color and general aspect. Culms short and densely tufted to tall, coarse and few in a cluster, the culm height varying from 10 to over 90 cm. Herbage glabrous except for a few long hairs on the blade above and lateral to the ligule. Ligule a minute fringe of hairs. Spikelets many-flowered, laterally flattened, pale green or violet to reddish-brown, at maturity varying from 5 to 15 mm or more in

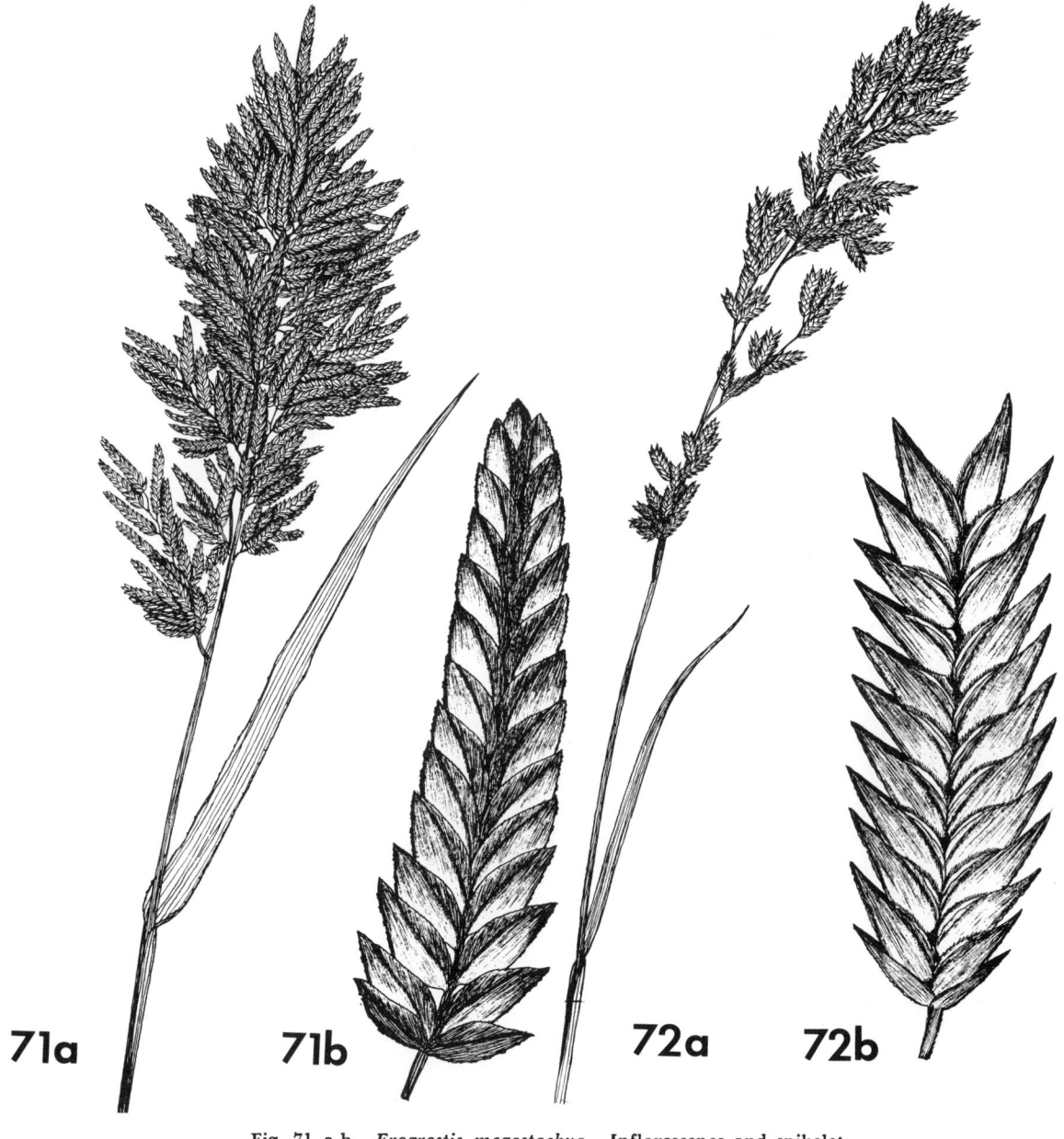

Fig. 71 a-b. *Erogrostis megastachya.* Inflorescence and spikelet.
Fig. 72 a-b. *Eragrostis oxylepis.* Inflorescence and spikelet.

length. Glumes and lemmas glabrous, sharply keeled. Lemmas strongly 3-nerved, usually 3-4 mm long. Occasional to frequent on sandy loam sites throughout our area but of little or no forage value.

*8. ERAGROSTIS SESSILISPICA Buckl. TUMBLE LOVEGRASS (Fig. 73). Native warm-season perennial with wiry culms and large, little-branched inflorescences. Ligule a ring of hairs 2-3 mm long. Inflorescence 15-30 cm or more long, over half the length of the culm, breaking off at maturity and becoming a tumbleweed. Spikelets sessile on and appressed to stiff, curving inflorescence branches. An "increaser" on disturbed sites, this grass is most frequent on heavily grazed open sandy prairies. It has little forage value.

*9. ERAGROSTIS SILVEANA Swallen. SILVEUS LOVEGRASS. Native warm-season perennial. Infrequent, usually associated with buffalograss and other short grasses on open prairie sites.

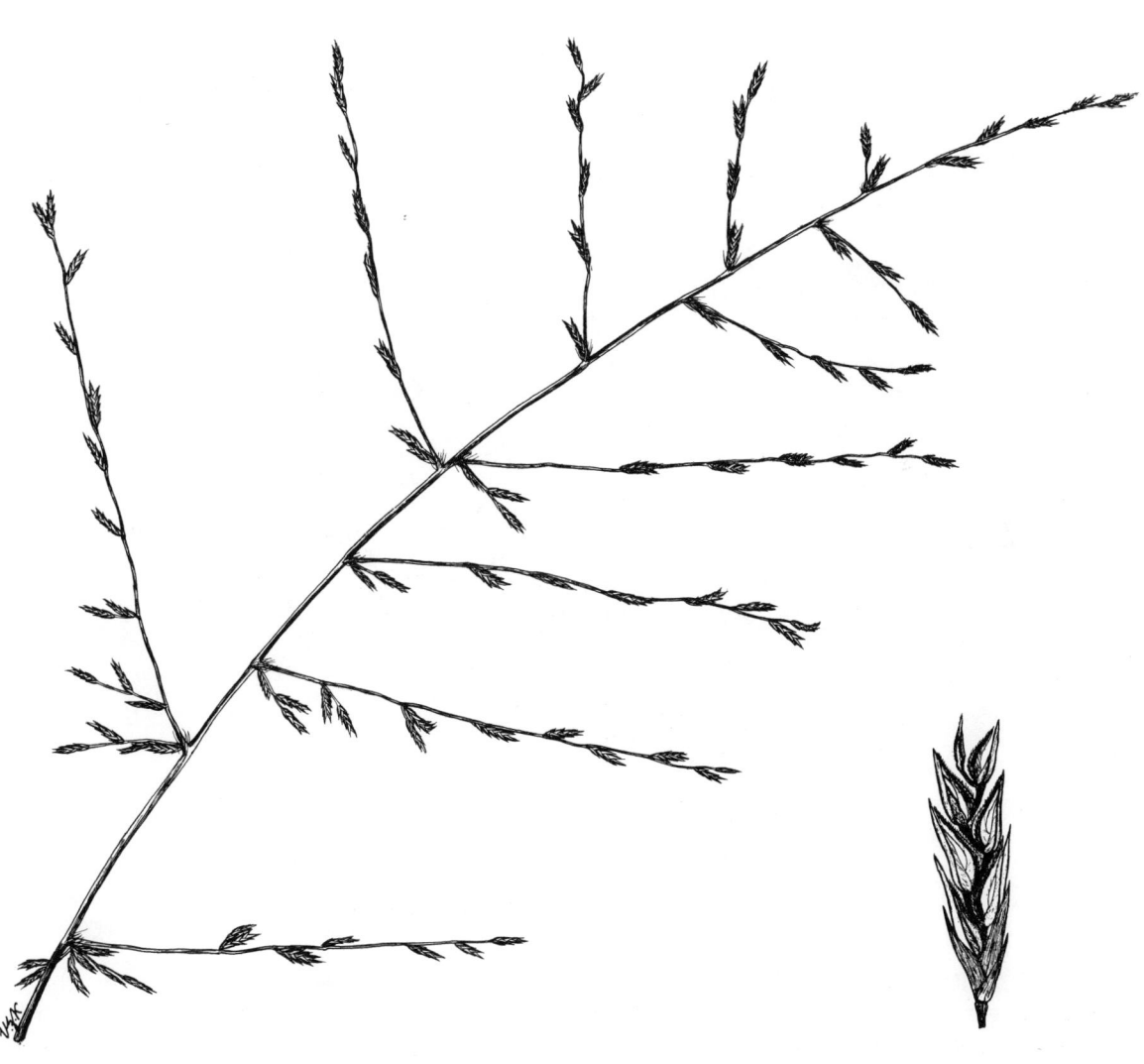

Fig. 73. *Eragrostis sessilispica*. Inflorescence and spikelet.

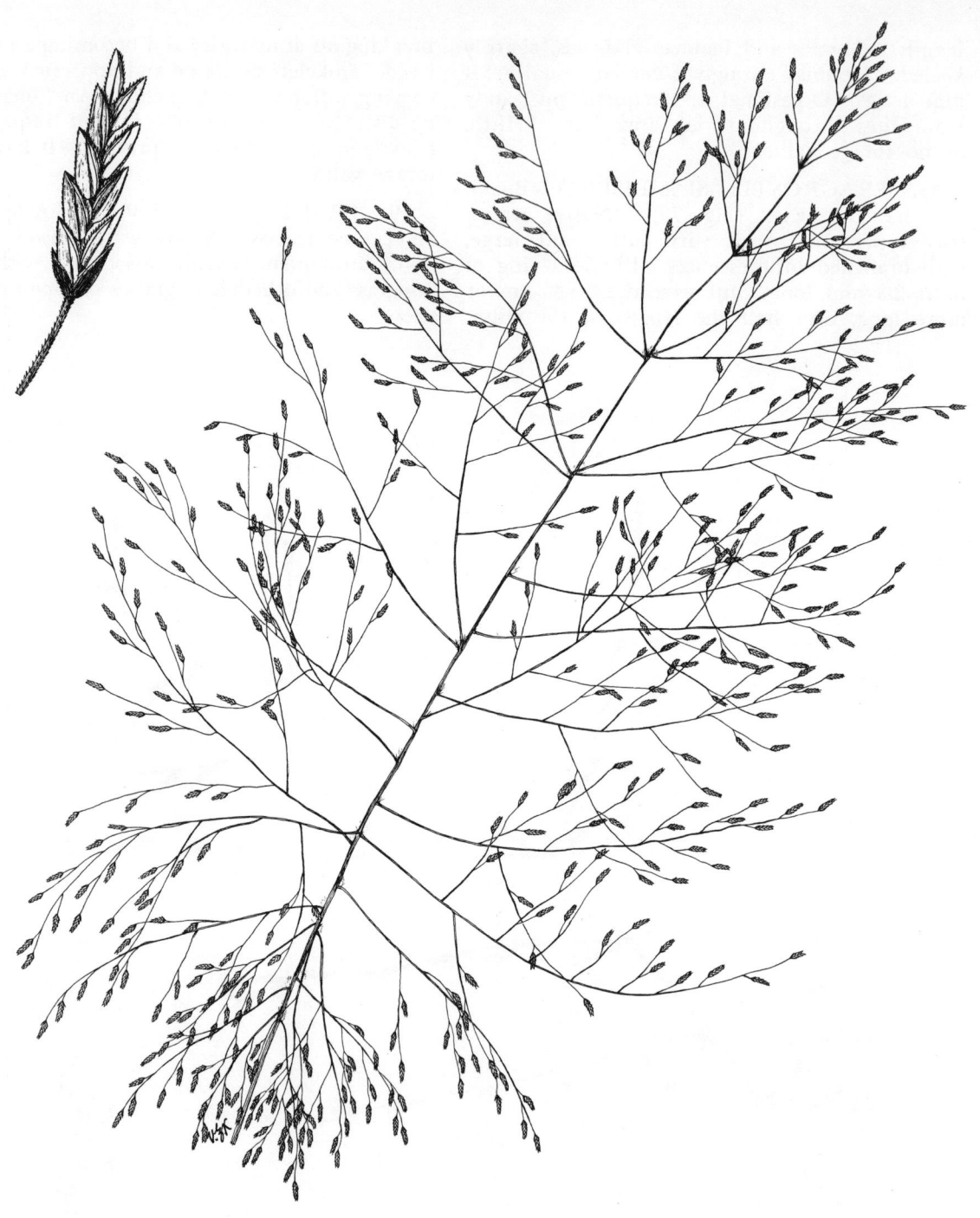

Fig. 74. *Eragrostis spectabilis*. Inflorescence and spikelet.

10. ERAGROSTIS SPECTABILIS (Pursh) Steud. PURPLE LOVEGRASS (Fig. 74). Native warm-season perennial bunchgrass, with large, many-flowered panicles. The inflorescence readily breaks off at the base and becomes a tumbleweed at maturity. Occasional on sandy sites, especially in open woodlands. With little or no forage value.

11. ERAGROSTIS SWALLENI Hitchc. SWALLEN LOVEGRASS. Native warm-season perennial bunchgrass. With a restricted range of from South Texas to northern Mexico, this grass is reported by Jones *et al.* (1961) to be frequent on sandy loam soils in Kleberg County.

24. ERIOCHLOA Cupgrass

Caespitose warm-season annuals and perennials. Inflorescence of a few to several short subspicate branches. First glume reduced to a cup or disc. Second glume and sterile lemma about equal, acuminate. Fertile lemma minutely rugose, apiculate or short-awned.

A genus of about 20 species, these mostly in the warmer regions of the Americas.

KEY TO THE SPECIES

Pedicels glabrous or minutely puberulent; fertile lemma with an awn of 0.5-1.5 mm long
  Spikelet 4-5 mm long; awn of fertile lemma 1 mm or more long; plants perennial   *E. punctata*
  Spikelets 3.5-4 mm long; awn of fertile lemma mostly 0.5-0.8 mm long; plants annual *E. contracta*
Pedicels with hairs about half as long as the spikelet; fertile lemma awnless or with an awn less than 0.5 mm long; perennial   *E. sericea*

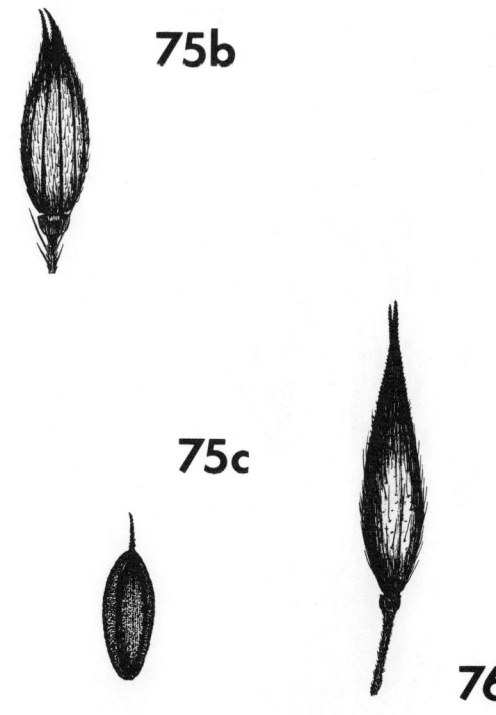

Fig. 75 a-c. *Eriochloa contracta*. Plant, spikelet and fertile floret.

Fig. 76. *Eriochloa punctata*. Spikelet.

*1. ERIOCHLOA CONTRACTA Hitchc. PRAIRIE CUPGRASS (Fig. 75). Native warm-season annual. Culms mostly 40-80 cm tall. Blades usually not more than 5 mm broad. Occasional in moist sandy sites in our area. Of little forage significance.

*2. ERIOCHLOA PUNCTATA (L.) Desv. LOUISIANA CUPGRASS (Fig. 76). Coarse native warm-season perennial, with thick, usually decumbent culms to 110 cm or more long and flat blades mostly 5-10 mm broad. Occasional in swales, ditches, and similar moist habitats.

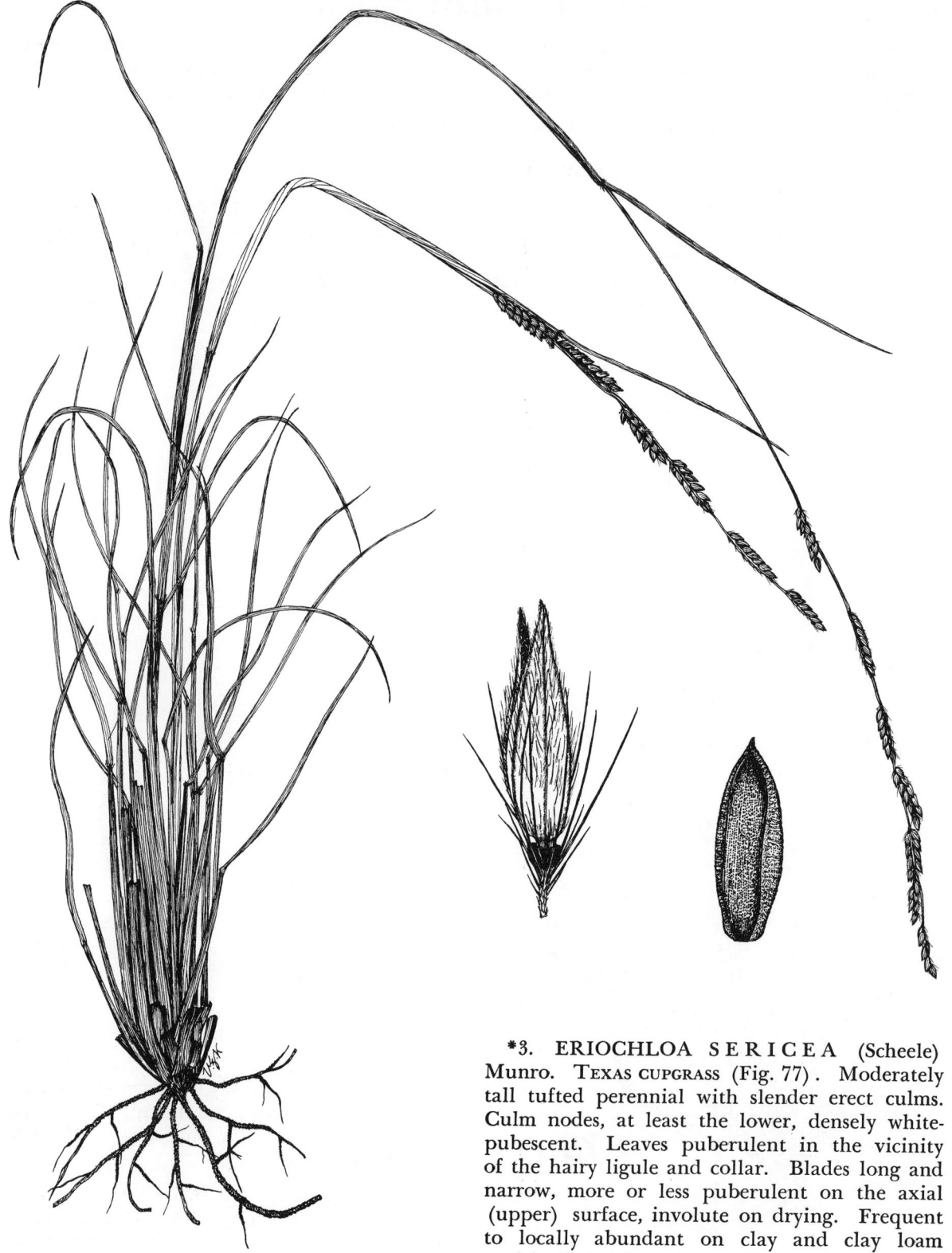

Fig. 77. *Eriochloa sericea*. Plant, spikelet and fertile floret.

*3. ERIOCHLOA SERICEA (Scheele) Munro. Texas cupgrass (Fig. 77). Moderately tall tufted perennial with slender erect culms. Culm nodes, at least the lower, densely white-pubescent. Leaves puberulent in the vicinity of the hairy ligule and collar. Blades long and narrow, more or less puberulent on the axial (upper) surface, involute on drying. Frequent to locally abundant on clay and clay loam prairie sites. A native prairie species that persists in heavily grazed pastures only in protection of shrubs.

hairyness of the lemma, hairyness of the palea, shape of the bicellular microscopic epidermal hairs, leaf anatomy, general plant habit and height, and nature of the panicle.

1. ERIONEURON PILOSUM (Buckl.) Nash *(Tridens pilosus* (Buckl.) Hitchc.). (Fig. 78). Low tufted perennial, with short, contracted, few-flowered inflorescences of large, pubescent spikelets. In dry open sites, usually on sandy soils. Reported by Jones *et al.* (1961) to occur in our area.

26. FESTUCA Fescue

Spikelets few- to several-flowered, disarticulating above the glumes. Glumes unequal, shorter than the lower lemma. Lemma 5-nerved, awnless or awned from the usually entire tip.

A genus of about 80 caespitose perennial species, widely distributed in the temperate and colder regions of the world. Most fescues are of good forage value when sufficiently abundant. The common annual "sixweeks fescue," *Festuca octoflora* Walt. of Hitchcocks Manual (1950), is herein referred to the genus *Vulpia*.

1. FESTUCA ARUNDINACEAE Schreb. TALL FESCUE. Blades flat, 4-8 mm wide. Panicle erect or drooping, 10-20 cm long. Spikelets 8-12 mm long. Introduced cool-season pasture grass. Occasional in ditches and roadsides along the Gulf Coast but without definite record in the Coastal Bend region.

27. HETEROPOGON

Caespitose annuals and perennials, lacking rhizomes or stolons. A genus of about 7 species, widely distributed in the warmer regions of the world.

Fig. 78. *Erioneuron pilosum.* Inflorescence and spikelet.

25. ERIONEURON

A genus of five North American species, which until recently have been placed in the genus *Tridens*. The generic name was first proposed by Nash (in Small, 1903). The Japanese worker Tuguo Tateoka in a recent study of the group (1961) noted numerous differences between *Erioneuron* and *Tridens*, including the basic chromosome number, shape and color of the caryopsis, color of the stigma, shape and

*1. HETEROPOGON CONTORTUS (L.) Beauv. TANGLEHEAD (Fig. 79). Native warm-season perennial, with conspicuous long, dark, geniculate-twisted awns and flattened, keeled leaf-sheaths. Widespread in the subtropics and tropics of both hemispheres, this grass is occasional to frequent in the coastal prairies. Although tanglehead probably once contributed greatly to the composition of the vegetation of the Coastal Bend, it now persists only in well-managed pastures. It is rated as a "decreaser" of excellent forage value.

Fig. 79. *Heteropogon contortus*. Plant and seed-bearing spikelet.

28. HILARIA

Inflorescence a spike with spikelets in threes on a persistent zigzag rachis, the 3 spikelets disarticulating together. Lateral spikelets of group staminate, 2-flowered, central spikelet 1- (occasionally 2-) flowered, fertile. A genus of 8 or 10 species, distributed in the semi-arid regions of southwestern United States, Mexico and Central America. All species are warm-season perennials.

*1. HILARIA BELANGERI (Steud.) Nash. CURLYMESQUITE (Fig. 80). Plants low, stoloniferous, sod-forming. Frequent to locally abundant on clay prairie sites, apparently favored by heavy grazing. Although often associated with buffalograss, curlymesquite appears to make best yields on well-drained land, while buffalograss grows better on tight, impermeable clays. These two grasses are similar vegetatively but curlymesquite can be distinguished by the pubescent culms nodes. *Hilaria belangeri* is of only fair grazing value.

Fig. 80. *Hilaria belangeri*. Plant and two views of spikelet cluster.

29. HORDEUM Barley

Spikelets 1-flowered (rarely 2-flowered), three at each node of a short, readily disarticulating rachis, the lateral spikelets reduced and sterile (except in the cultivated barley, *H. vulgare*).

A genus of about 25 species, native to temperate regions of both hemispheres. Except for *H. vulgare*, the genus is of little economic value. Our species are cool-season annuals.

KEY TO THE SPECIES

Lateral spikelets pedicelled, reduced and sterile
    Leaves with slender auricles; glumes of the fertile spikelet and inner glumes of the lateral spikelets not strikingly broadened above the base; lemma of central spikelet with awns 2.5-4.0 cm long   *H. leporinum*
    Leaves without auricles; glumes of the fertile spikelet and inner glumes of the lateral spikelets strikingly broadened above the base; lemma of the central spikelet with awns 0.7-1.5 cm long   *H. pusillum*
Lateral spikelets sessile, similar to the middle one and fertile   *H. vulgare*

1. HORDEUM LEPORINUM Link. HARE BARLEY (Fig. 81). Glumes of central spikelet long-ciliate on both margins. This introduced annual is a common weed in North Texas and has been reported as far south as San Antonio. It has not been recorded from the Coastal Bend area but is to be expected on roadsides and similar disturbed sites.

*2. HORDEUM PUSILLUM Nutt. LITTLE BARLEY (Fig. 82). Short-lived low, slender, native annual. Locally frequent in early spring on road-ways, ant beds and other disturbed sites, often associated with *Vulpia octoflora*.

*3. HORDEUM VULGARE L. BARLEY (Fig. 83). Culms stout, succulent, mostly 50-90 cm tall. Leaves with well-developed auricles and broad, flat blades. Barley is rather frequent on roadsides and along field borders from chance seedings but is unable to persist out of cultivation.

30. LEERSIA Cutgrass

A genus of about 10 species, five in the United States. Similar to the closely related cultivated rice, *Oryza sativa*, these warm-season perennials for the most part are adapted to moist or marshy habitats.

KEY TO THE SPECIES

Spikelets 3.5-5 mm long and 1.5-2 mm broad; spikelets appressed on the branches or somewhat spreading   *L. hexandra*
Spikelets 2-3 mm long and 1 mm or less broad; spikelets closely appressed to the branches
    Spikelets broadly ovate, glabrous, about 2 mm long; culms erect; rhizomes absent *L. monandra*
    Spikelets oblong, finely hispid, about 3 mm long; culms decumbent at base; rhizomes developed   *L. virginica*

*1. LEERSIA HEXANDRA Swartz. CLUBHEAD CUTGRASS (Fig 84). Plants with slender creeping rhizomes. Culms decumbent at base. Leaf blades mostly 2-5 mm broad. Panicles mostly 5-8 cm long, the branches short and stiffly erect. Clubhead cutgrass is locally frequent in moist sandy soils or in pond microsites throughout the area, often growing in water around tanks, drains and creeks. It is of little grazing value.

*2. LEERSIA MONANDRA Swartz. BUNCH CUTGRASS (Fig. 85). Plants without rhizomes. Culms slender wiry, stiffly erect, 50-100 cm tall. Occasional on well-drained, clay or clay loam prairie sites. Bunch cutgrass disappears under heavy grazing and persists only in protection of shrubs in heavily utilized pastures.

3. LEERSIA VIRGINICA Willd. WHITEGRASS (Fig. 86). Plants with stout rhizomes. Culms slender, weak, as much as 100 cm tall. Blades short, usually 6-12 mm long. In low moist sites, often in woodlands. Infrequent in our area.

Fig. 81. *Hordeum leporinum*. Inflorescence and 3 spikelets at node of rachis

Fig. 82. *Hordeum pusillum.* Plant and spikelet cluster.

Fig. 83. *Hordeum vulgare*. Plant and spikelet cluster.

Fig. 84. *Leersia hexandra*. Plant and spikelet.

Fig. 85 a-b. *Leersia monandra*. Inflorescence and spikelet.
Fig. 86 a-b. *Leersia virginica*. Inflorescence and spikelet.

31. LEPTOCHLOA Sprangletop

Inflorescence with few to several spicate branches, these clustered at the culm apex or scattered. Spikelets 2-several-flowered, disarticulating above the glumes. Lemmas strongly 3-nerved, the nerves often short-awned or minutely mucronate. Annual and perennial bunchgrasses, with erect culms mostly 30-100 cm tall and erect or nodding inflorescences.

Species about 20, in the tropics and subtropics of both hemispheres. Of the 11 species reported for the United States, only one, *L. dubia,* is of significance as a forage grass. In Texas these are warm-season grasses.

KEY TO THE SPECIES

Apex of lemma broad, notched, awnless; lemmas 3.5-5 mm long *L. dubia*
Apex of lemmas acute or awned, or if broad and awnless then lemmas 3 mm or less long

Spikelets 2 mm or less long, with mostly 2-3 (rarely 1-4) florets; lemmas awnless; leaf sheaths papillose-hispid or pilose; slender weedy annual of disturbed soils *L. filiformis*
Spikelets more than 2 mm long or plant large and coarse
　Spikelets 2-4 mm long
　　Inflorescence axis usually 30 cm or more long, bearing numerous short, stiff, erect branches mostly 2-4 cm long; large coarse annual *L. nealleyi*
　　Inflorescence axis less than 30 cm long, the branches typically slender and somewhat flexuous, 5-10 cm or more long; perennial *L. domingensis*
　Spikelets 5-10 mm long
　　Lemmas short-awned from a narrow, usually bifid apex; second glume 3-4 mm long *L. fascicularis*
　　Lemmas awnless or mucronate, the apex broad; second glume less than 3 mm long; panicle lead-colored *L. uninervia*

Fig. 87. *Leptochloa domingensis*. Inflorescence and spikelet.

*1. **LEPTOCHLOA DOMINGENSIS** (Jacq.) Trin. DOMINICAN SPRANGLETOP (Fig. 87). Tall native perennial. Occasional in sandy and sandy loam savannah sites, often in the shade of oaks but seldom in dense motts.

2. **LEPTOCHLOA DUBIA** (H.B.K.) Nees. GREEN SPRANGLETOP (Fig. 88). Native perennial with glabrous sheaths and flat or somewhat involute blades. Inflorescence of 3 to several racemosely arranged branches 4-12 cm or more in length. Cleistogamous spikelets regularly are produced in the axils of the leaf-sheath.

This valuable range forage grass apparently is infrequent in the Texas Coastal Bend area. It is best adapted to sandy or sandy loam sites.

*3. **LEPTOCHLOA FASCICULARIS** (Lam.) Gray. BEARDED SPRANGLETOP (Fig. 89). Native annual. Occasional in moist sandy and sandy loam sites, commonly growing near the water's edge in sandy lakes. Of fair grazing value.

4. **LEPTOCHLOA FILIFORMIS** (Lam.) Beauv. RED SPRANGLETOP (Fig. 90). Native annual with slender, rather widely spaced inflorescence branches. Red sprangletop is a common weed of roadsides, barnyards, and other disturbed sites. The plant may vary from 20 cm or less tall to over 70 cm tall.

*5. **LEPTOCHLOA NEALLEYI** Vasey. NEALLEY SPRANGLETOP (Fig. 91). Robust annual with culms commonly 1 meter or more in height. Usually growing in moist sandy or sandy loam sites, this species is most frequent in roadside ditches and along ponds.

*6. **LEPTOCHLOA UNINERVIA** (Presl.) Hitchc. and Chase. MEXICAN SPRANGLETOP (Fig. 92). Native annual, weedy in general aspect and usually growing in moist or wet clay soils near water.

Fig. 88. *Leptochloa dubia*. Inflorescence and spikelet.

Fig. 89 a-b. *Leptochloa fascicularis*. Inflorescence and spikelet.
Fig. 90 a-b. *Leptochloa filiformis*. Inflorescence and spikelet.

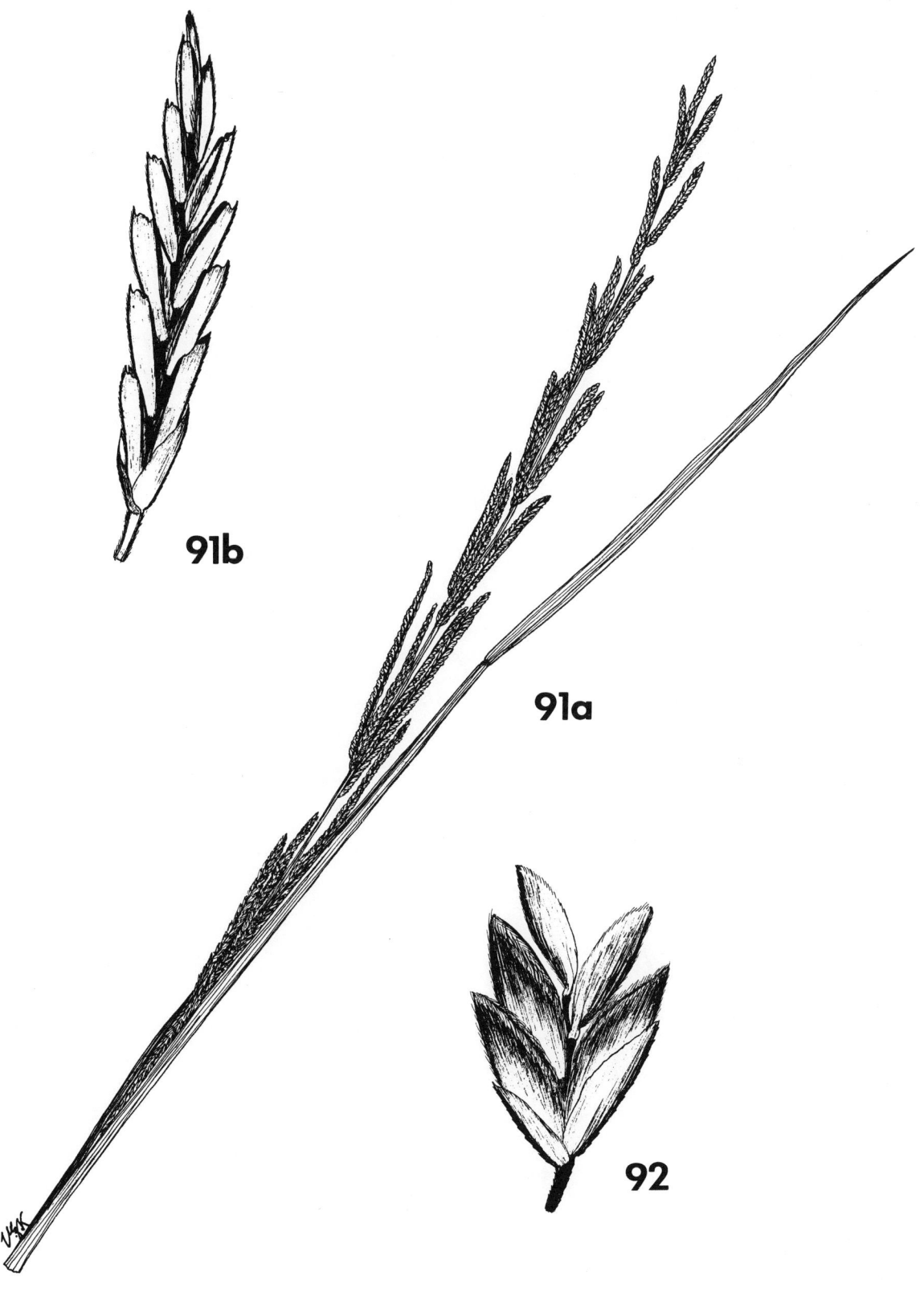

Fig. 91 a-b. *Leptochloa nealleyi*. Inflorescence and spikelet.
Fig. 92. *Leptochloa uninervia*. Spikelet.

Fig. 93. *Leptoloma cognatum*. Plant and spikelet.

32. LEPTOLOMA Witchgrass

A small genus of panicoid grasses, represented in the United States by the two species of our area. These grasses are included in the genus *Digitaria* by some authors.

KEY TO THE SPECIES

Creeping rhizomes developed .... *L. arenicola*

Creeping rhizomes absent .... *L. cognatum*

1. **LEPTOLOMA ARENICOLA** Swallen. SAND WITCHGRASS. A native warm-season endemic, known only from the sand hills along the Gulf. In Hitchcock's Manual the spikelet length is stated to be 4 mm but specimens from Padre Island and Flour Bluff (near Corpus Christi) have spikelets only about 3 mm long. The basis for separation of *L. arenicola* from the polymorphic and widely distributed *L. cognatum* appears relatively "weak" and the two perhaps represent a single species.

*2. **LEPTOLOMA COGNATUM** (Schult.) Chase. FALL WITCHGRASS (Fig. 93). Culm slender, wiry, from a knotty, usually densely hairy base. Inflorescence an open panicle with long-pedicelled spikelets 2.5-3.0 mm long. Nerves of the second glume and sterile lemma sparsely to densely pubescent. A native warm-season perennial that is occasional on well-drained sandy or sandy loam sites, usually in moderately disturbed open prairies.

33. LIMNODIA

A monotypic North American genus, with the single species distributed from Florida to Arkansas and Texas.

*1. **LIMNODIA ARKANSANA** (Nutt.) L. H. Dewey. OZARKGRASS (Fig. 94). Native, short-lived, cool-season annual. Leaf blades thin, flat. Ligule a fringed membrane about 1 mm long. Inflorescence a loosely contracted panicle. Spikelets 1-flowered, disarticulating below the glumes. Glumes firm, equal, as large as the lemma. Lemma membraneous, glabrous, nerveless, 2-toothed at apex and bearing a delicate awn between the teeth. Growing in disturbed areas of most soil types, this grass is commonly associated with *Vulpia octoflora* and *Hordeum pusillum*.

Fig. 94. *Limnodia arkansana*. Inflorescence (a), spikelet (b), and floret (c).

34. LOLIUM Ryegrass

Inflorescence a spike. Spikelets large, several-flowered, oriented edgewise to the rachis. First glume lacking except on the terminal spikelet. Disarticulation above the glumes. A genus of 6-8 species, with natural distribution in the temperate and cooler regions of Europe and Asia.

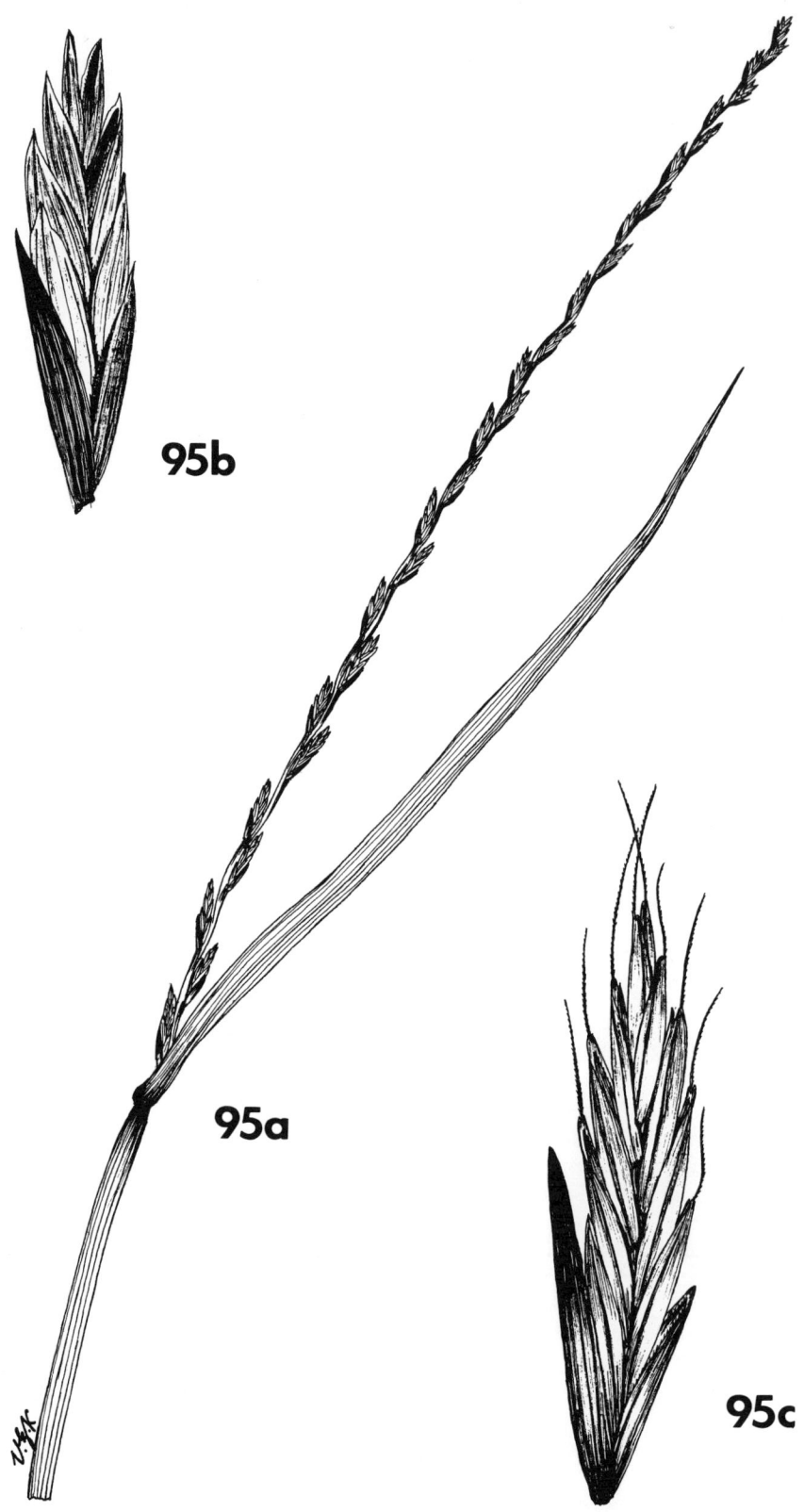

Fig. 95. *Lolium perenne*. Inflorescence (a), terminal spikelet with awnless lemmas (b), terminal spikelet with awned lemmas (c).

KEY TO THE SPECIES

Glume equalling or exceeding the terminal floret   *L. temulentum*
Glume not equalling or exceeding the terminal floret   *L. perenne*

*1. LOLIUM PERENNE L. PERENNIAL RYE (Fig. 95). Introduced cool-season weak perennial or annual with bright green, rather succulent herbage. Leaf blades flat, glabrous. Inflorescence normally a spike with one spikelet per node. Spikelets large, flattened, several-flowered. Lemmas mostly 5-7 mm long, awnless or with a fine, slender awn. Included here are plants commonly referred to *Lolium multiflorum* Lam. (Italian rye) which with us is primarily distinguished by having awned rather than awnless lemmas. Awn length in our plants is extremely variable and does not appear to be correlated with other plant characters.

Perennial rye was the first meadow grass to be cultivated in Europe as a distinct segregrated species (Hitchcock, 1950). It is seeded as a cool-season forage grass in many areas of Texas and also is used for winter lawns. In our area, perennial rye occurs mainly as a weed of pasture borders, roadsides and other disturbed sites.

2. LOLIUM TEMULENTUM L. DARNEL. A cool-season annual that is occasional throughout much of the United States as a roadside weed. In the Coastal Bend this grass is known only from a recent collection made near Tivoli. The plants of this collection (*Gould 9891*) have long-awned lemmas and thus are referrable to the var. *temulentum*. Plants with awnless lemmas, referrable of the var. *leptochaeton* A. Br., also occur in Texas.

35. MANISURIS Jointtail

A tropical-subtropical genus of about 30 species, five in the United States. All species are perennial, with inflorescences reduced to spikes or spikelike racemes and with the spikelets partially sunken in a thickened rachis. The spikelets are in pairs of one sessile and fertile and one pedicelled and sterile.

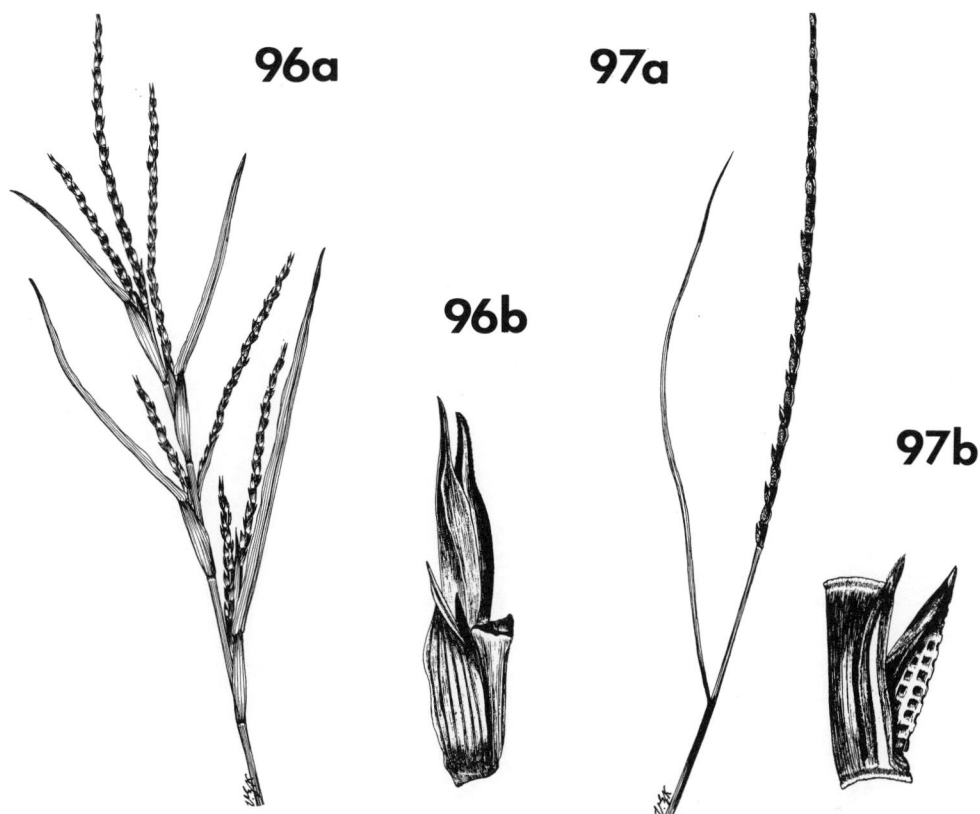

Fig. 96 a-b. *Manisuris altissima*. Inflorescence and spikelet pair on section of rachis.
Fig. 97 a-b. *Manisuris cylindrica*. Inflorescence and spikelet pair on section of rachis.

KEY TO THE SPECIES

Racemes flattened; first glume of sessile spikelet smooth — *M. altissima*

Racemes cylindrical; first glume of sessile spikelet pitted along the nerves — *M. cylindrica*

1. **MANISURIS ALTISSIMA** (Poir.) Hitchc. AFRICAN JOINTTAIL (Fig. 96). Culms decumbent at base, flattened, 40-80 cm long, freely branching above. Sessile spikelets awnless, 5-7 mm long. Introduced warm-season perennial, infrequent in our area. Present for the most part on moist ditchbanks and other disturbed areas.

*2. **MANISURIS CYLINDRICA** (Michx.) Kuntze. CAROLINA JOINTTAIL (Fig. 97). Culms erect, tufted, 30-100 cm tall, little-branched. Sessile spikelet awnless, 4-5 mm long. Native warm-season perennial. Occasional in sandy loam and clay loam sites, usually growing in small colonies in lightly grazed pastures. A good forage grass.

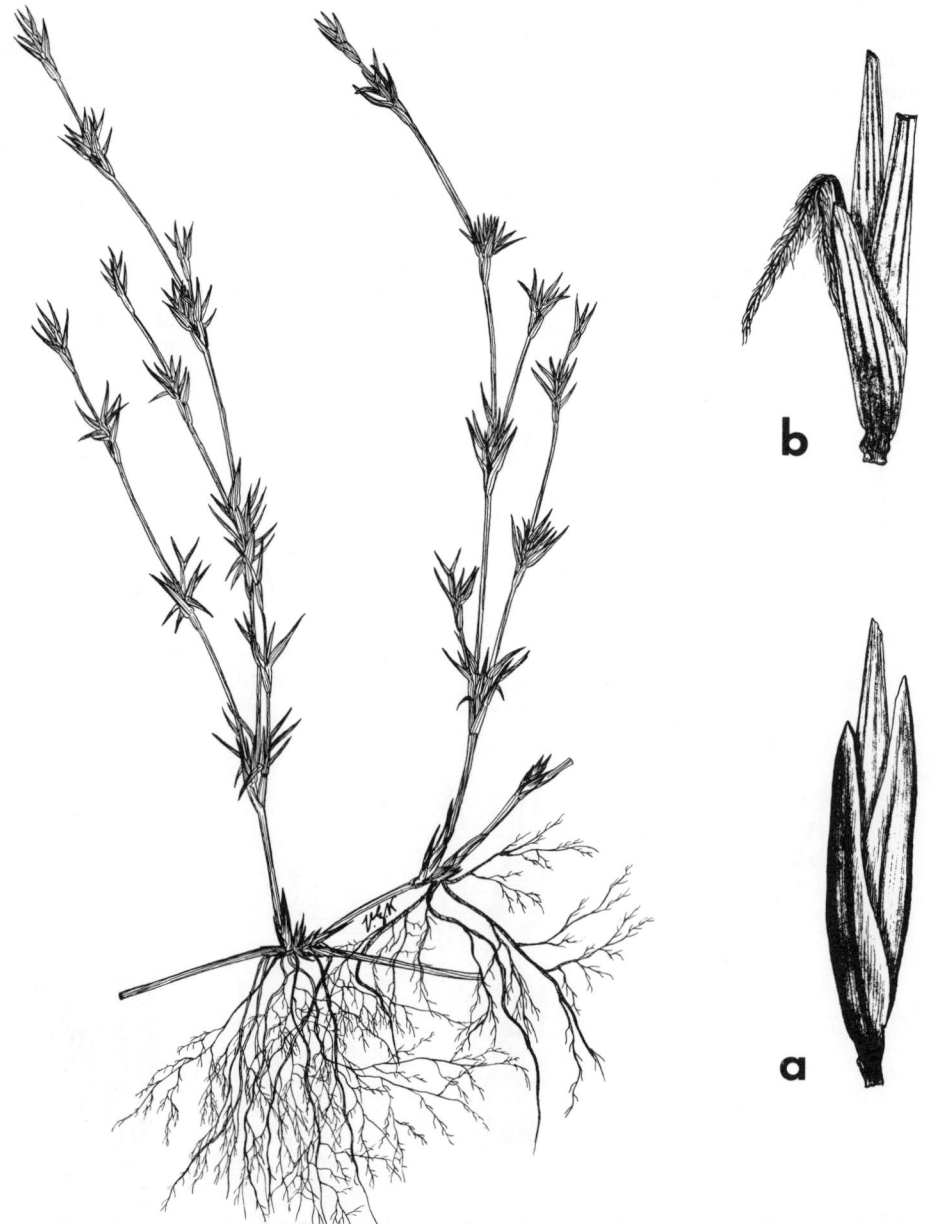

Fig. 98. *Monanthochloe littoralis*. Plant with staminate spikelet (a) and pistillate spikelet (b).

36. MONANTHOCHLOE

Plants dioecious, with small 3-5 flowered spikelets hidden in the leaf sheaths. Glumes absent. Lemmas several-nerved, those of the pistillate spikelet like the leaf blades in texture. A genus of two species, one in southeastern North America and Central America and the other in Argentina.

*1. MONANTHOCHLOE LITTORALIS Engelm. SHOREGRASS (Fig. 98). Native warm-season perennial. This low dioecious, mat-forming grass is locally abundant on saline sites and is the only grass on many of the salt-flat areas along the coast. It grows both on sandy and muddy sites. Shoregrass produces little palatable forage and is of poor grazing value.

37. MUHLENBERGIA Muhly

Inflorescence an open or contracted panicle. Spikelets one-flowered, disarticulating above the glumes. Glumes usually unequal and shorter than the lemma. Lemma firm, 3-nerved, awned from the tip or less frequently, awnless. As commonly interpreted, a group of some 120 species, these mostly in North America and western South America. With 44 species in the Arizona flora (Gould, 1951), *Muhlenbergia* is the largest grass genus of that state. The species of our area are native warm-season perennials.

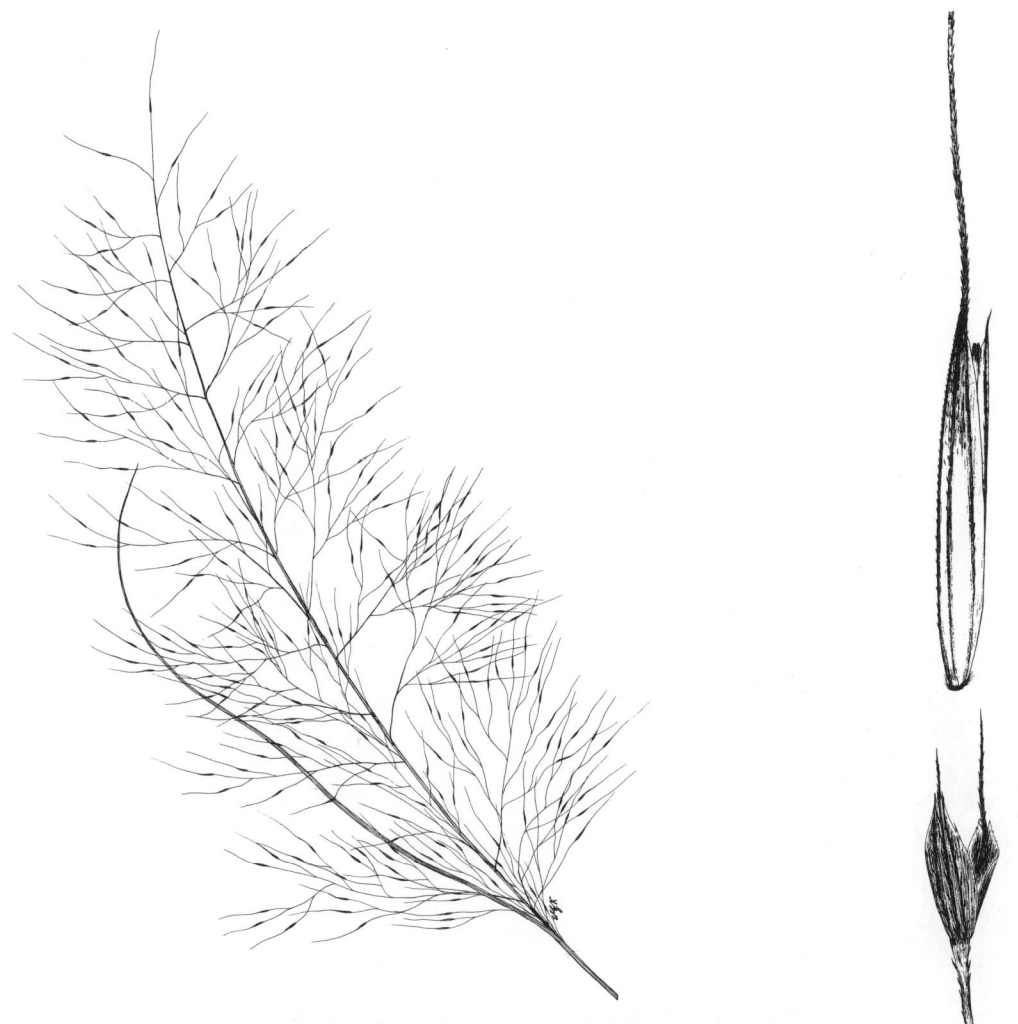

Fig. 99. *Muhlenbergia capillaris*. Inflorescence and spikelet with glumes separated from floret.

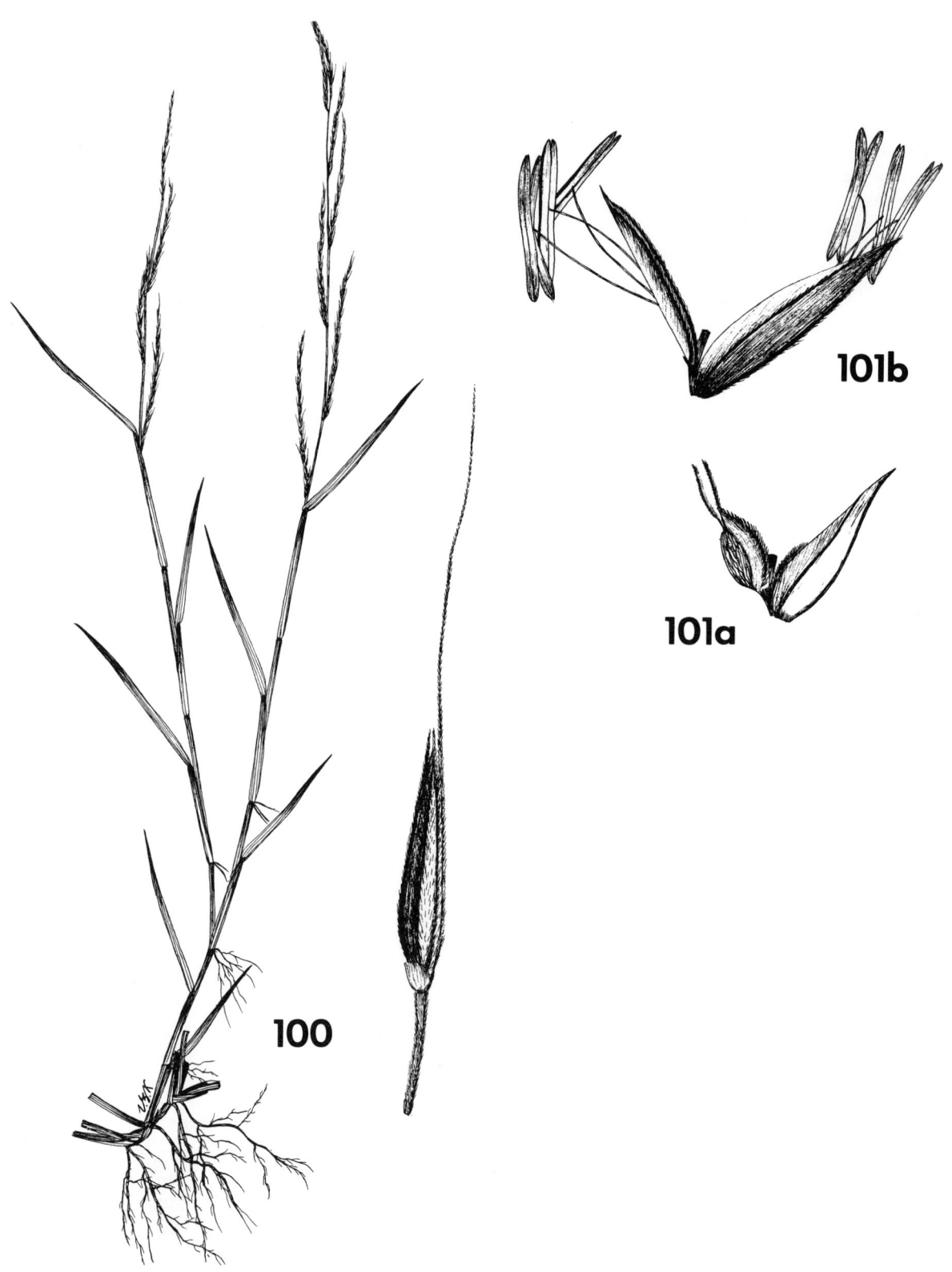

Fig. 100. *Muhlenbergia schreberi*. Plant and spikelet.
Fig. 101 a-b. *Neeragrostis reptans*. Pistillate florets (a), the upper with the lemma removed, and staminate florets (b), the upper with the lemmas removed.

KEY TO THE SPECIES

Panicle open, the spikelets on long pedicels   *M. capillaris*
Panicle contracted, the spikelets on short, appressed pedicels   *M. schreberi*

1. MUHLENBERGIA CAPILLARIS (Lam.) Trin. HAIRYAWN MUHLY (Fig. 99). Tufted bunch-grass with a large diffusely branched panicle. Reported by Jones et al. (1961) to occur in our area "in sandy openings in live oak woods."

2. MUHLENBERGIA SCHREBERI Gmel. NIMBLEWILL (Fig. 100). Culms slender, decumbent, creeping, often rooting at the nodes, 10-30 cm long. In sandy soil, usually in partial shade. Infrequent in our area.

38. NEERAGROSTIS

A monotypic genus, the sole representative of which is distributed from Kentucky and Florida to South Dakota, Texas and northern Mexico. It also has been reported from Surinam. Hitchcock (1926, 1950) did not recognize this genus and treated the species as *Eragrostis reptans* (Michx.) Nees. Nicora (1962) reviewed the characteristics of the taxon and concluded that it was distinct from *Eragrostis*. Differences in ovary and epidermal characters were noted as well as the dioecious nature of the former. Nicora noted similarities and probably close relationships between *Neeragrostis* and the genera *Distichlis* and *Monanthochloe*.

*1. NEERAGROSTIS REPTANS (Michx.) Nicora. *(Eragrostis reptans* (Michx.) Nees) (Fig. 101). Stoloniferous, dioecious, mat-forming, warm-season annual. Leaves minutely puberulent. Sheaths short, membranous on the margins below. Ligule a minute fringe of hairs. Spikelets borne in irregular clusters on slender culms mostly 5-10 cm tall. Anthers 1.5-1.8 mm long.

Locally abundant on poorly drained sites with fine-textured soils. This grass, commonly known as "creeping lovegrass," frequently is present in solid stands in "hog wallows" and drying lake beds.

39. OPLISMENUS Basketgrass

Spikelets subsessile, crowded on short inflorescence branches. Glumes about equal, awned. Sterile lemma longer than the glumes and fertile lemma, awned or mucronate. Fertile lemma smooth, elliptic, acute at apex, with the firm margins clasping but not inrolled over the palea.

About 10 species, in the tropics and subtropics of both hemispheres but none native to the United States. Both of the species that have been introduced into southern United States are perennial, with slender decumbent stoloniferous culms that root freely at the nodes.

KEY TO THE SPECIES

Inflorescence branches, at least the lower, 10-30 mm long, bearing 8 or more spikelets   *O. hirtellus*
Inflorescence branches mostly 2-3 mm long, bearing usually 3-5 spikelets   *O. setarius*

*1. OPLISMENUS HIRTELLUS (L.) Beauv. BASKETGRASS. Introduced warm-season perennial with weak, spreading stoloniferous culms. Infrequent, growing as a casual weed in our area.

2. OPLISMENUS SETARIUS (Lam.) Roem. and Schult. BRISTLE BASKETGRASS (Fig. 102). Introduced warm-season perennial, similar to *O. hirtellus* in general habit and also infrequent in our area.

40. ORYZA Rice

A genus of about 15 species, these adapted to moist or marshy tropical-subtropical habitats of both the Old and New World.

1. ORYZA SATIVA L. RICE (Fig. 103). Tall, erect annual with broad flat blades and drooping panicles of short-pedicelled, one-flowered spikelets. The caryopsis is tightly enclosed in a thick firm, flattened lemma, this awnless or short-awned. At the base of the lemma are two short bracts which superficially appear to be glumes but which have been interpreted as representing reduced lemmas of rudimentary florets (the true glumes thus absent). Rice is a major crop plant along the upper Texas gulf coast prairie and occurs sparingly as an escape along sloughs and marshy roadside ditches.

Fig. 102. *Oplismenus setarius*. Plant and spikelet.   Fig. 103. *Oryza sativa*. Inflorescence and spikelet.

41. PANICUM

A genus of about 500 tropical and subtropical grasses, with some 170 species in the United States and over 90 in Texas. Our species belong to two large and rather well-defined subgenera, Subgenus Dicanthelium and Subgenus Eupanicum. Species referred to Subgenus Paurochaetium in Hitchcock's Manual are herein included in *Setaria*.

All North American panicums basically are warm-season grasses but those of the Dicanthelium subgenus flower relatively early in the spring and then again in late summer or fall. Taxonomically the Dicanthelium panicums are one of the most difficult of all United States grass groups.

KEY TO THE SPECIES

Plants forming a winter rosette of short basal leaves; spikelets ovate, oblong, obovate or obpyriform, blunt at the apex; tufted native perennials, lacking rhizomes or stolons and mostly with short leaf blades; panicles open, relatively small, infrequently over 10 cm long   A.

Plants not forming a winter rosette of basal leaves; annuals and perennials, with open or contracted panicles   AA.

A. (Subgenus Dicanthelium)

Spikelets 2.5 mm or less long
  Culm nodes and usually the leaves conspicuously pubescent with long spreading hairs
                                                                                                 P. lanuginosum
  Culm nodes and leaves glabrous, minutely puberulent, or with a few long hairs
    Culms relatively stout, at least below; mid-culm blades mostly 6-15 mm broad and 7-15 cm long, cordate-clasping at the base; panicle many-flowered, usually 4-5 cm broad on the primary (spring) culms   *P. sphaerocarpon*
    Culms slender and wiry; mid-culm blades typically 2-4 mm broad
      Mid-culm blades linear, 1-4 mm broad and mostly 5-8 cm long; spikelets 2.0-2.2 mm long
                                                                  P. ovinum
      Mid-culm blades lanceolate, mostly 2-4 mm broad and 2-5 cm long; panicle few-flowered, mostly 2-3 cm broad; spikelets 1.5-1.8 mm long   *P. portericensis*
Spikelets 2.7-4.0 mm long
  Spikelets 2.7-3.3 mm long, oblong or obovate   *P. oligosanthes*
  Spikelets 3.7-4.0 mm long, narrowly obpyriform   *P. nodatum*

AA. (Subgenus Eupanicum)

Spikelets about 4 mm long, pyriform, broadening toward the apex; leaf blades 7 (rarely 10) cm or less long; low perennial with wiry, freely branched culms (a species of the Dicanthelium subgenus)   *P. nodatum*
Spikelets large or small but much less than 4 mm long when leaf blade is less than 10 cm long
  Culms stout, stiffly erect from a rhizomatous base; spikelets 3.5-6.5 mm long; second glume acute, more than half as long as the spikelet
    Culms 30 to about 100 cm tall, arising singly from the nodes of an extensive system of creeping rhizomes; spikelets 5.0-6.5 mm long; panicle contracted, not more than 3 cm wide   *P. amarum*
    Culms mostly 1-2 meters tall, in large dense clumps
      Inflorescence densely-flowered, mostly 5-10 cm wide; spikelets 4.3-5.5 mm long; plants of coastal sands   *P. amarulum*
      Inflorescence open, not densely-flowered; spikelets 3.5-5.0 mm long; plants of moist banks and swale areas, not on the coastal sands   *P. virgatum*
  Culms various, when stout and stiffly erect from a rhizomatous base then spikelets less than 3.5 mm long

Spikelets mostly 5-7 mm long
　Panicle open, with long spreading branches; fertile lemma smooth, less than half as long as the attenuate second glume and sterile lemma; perennial　　*P. capillarioides*
　Panicle contracted, the branches short and appressed; fertile lemma rugose, nearly as long as the second glume and sterile lemma; coarse annual　　*P. texanum*
Spikelets less than 4 mm long
　Spikelets tuberculate-hispid; culms slender and wiry, with many nodes and short internodes, freely branching above the base; leaf blades mostly 1.5-3.0 mm broad and 8-12 cm long　　*P. brachyanthum*
　Spikelets not tuberculate-hipsid
　　First glume obtuse, more than two-thirds as long as the spikelet; spikelets about 3.5 mm long; inflorescence contracted, the spikelets subsessile on short appressed branches; stoloniferous perennial　　*P. obtusum*
　　First glume less than two-thirds as long as the spikelet
　　　Inflorescence of 8 to 20 regularly spaced spicate branches, these mostly 2-3.5 cm long and bearing two rows of spikelets (similar to *Paspalum* in general appearance); stout perennials
　　　　Spikelets 2-2.4 mm long　　*P. geminatum*
　　　　Spikelets 2.5-3.0 mm long　　*P. paludivagum*
　　　Inflorescence not as above or plant annual
　　　　Fertile lemma rugose, with traverse ridges
　　　　　Spikelets 2.5-3.1 mm long; culms in tufts or bunches; leaf blades, at least some, 10-20 cm long
　　　　　　Plants perennial, with culms usually 1 meter or more tall; pedicels and branchlets glabrous　　*P. maximum*
　　　　　　Plants annual, with culms usually much less than 1 meter tall; pedicels or branchlets with scattered long stiff bristle-like hairs　　*P. fasciculatum*
　　　　　Spikelets about 2 mm long; culms decumbent, creeping, rooting at the nodes; leaf blades short, broad crisped on the margins, not over 6-9 cm long　*P. reptans*
　　　　Fertile lemma smooth
　　　　　Spikelets 2 mm or less long; in tight clusters along the primary panicle branches
　　　　　　Palea of the reduced floret large and firm, at maturity equalling or exceeding the fertile lemma in length; weak perennial with slender culms and flexible, usually spreading lower panicle branches　　*P. hians*
　　　　　　Palea of the reduced floret not large and firm, at maturity much shorter than the fertile lemma; culms relatively stout, from a hard base; inflorescence branches stiffly erect or erect-spreading　　*P. agrostoides*
　　　　　Spikelets more than 2 mm long
　　　　　　Culms 1-2 meters or more tall, becoming more or less woody in age, freely branching from swollen nodes, the internodes relatively short; spikelets mostly 2.5-3.0 mm long; non-rhizomatous perennial　　*P. antidotale*
　　　　　　Culms not becoming woody, if over 1 meter tall then trailing and decumbent and the nodes not swollen
　　　　　　　Plants annual, with thick, trailing or decumbent culms; first glume obtuse or rounded, about one-third as long as the spikelet　　*P. dichotomiflorum*
　　　　　　　Plants perennial, with erect culms; first glume acute, more than one-third as long as the spikelet
　　　　　　　　Panicle large, often half the length of the culm, diffuse, with stiffly spreading branches to 30 cm long, these often in groups of 2-4; culms stout, 70-100 cm tall　　*P. pilcomayense*
　　　　　　　　Panicle typically one-third to one-fourth the length of the culm, with erect-spreading branches developed singly at the nodes of the panicle axis; culms 15-80 cm tall
　　　　　　　　　Spikelets 2.1-2.7 mm long　　*P. filipes*
　　　　　　　　　Spikelets 3.0-3.7 mm long　　*P. hallii*

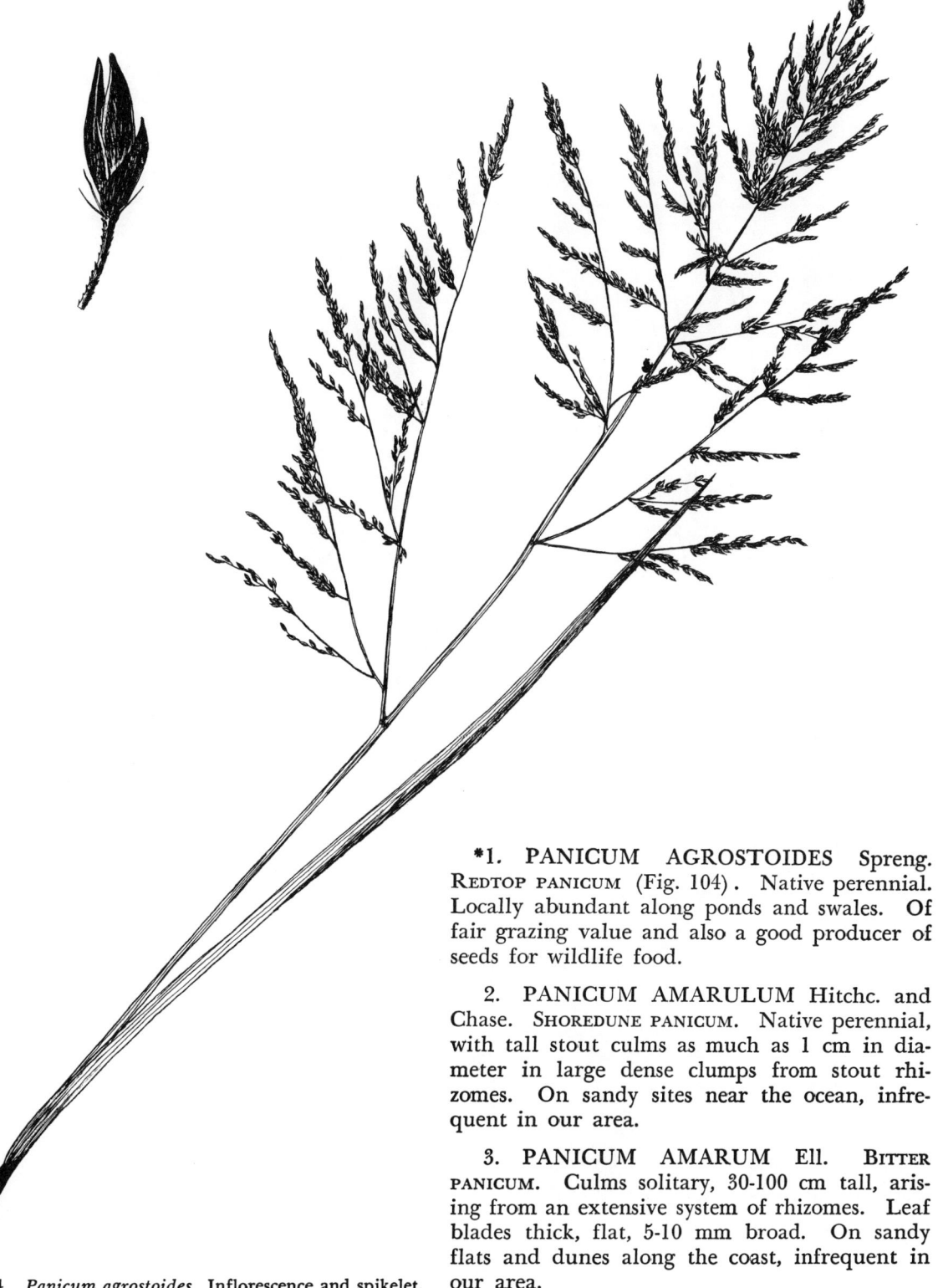

*1. PANICUM AGROSTOIDES Spreng. REDTOP PANICUM (Fig. 104). Native perennial. Locally abundant along ponds and swales. Of fair grazing value and also a good producer of seeds for wildlife food.

2. PANICUM AMARULUM Hitchc. and Chase. SHOREDUNE PANICUM. Native perennial, with tall stout culms as much as 1 cm in diameter in large dense clumps from stout rhizomes. On sandy sites near the ocean, infrequent in our area.

3. PANICUM AMARUM Ell. BITTER PANICUM. Culms solitary, 30-100 cm tall, arising from an extensive system of rhizomes. Leaf blades thick, flat, 5-10 mm broad. On sandy flats and dunes along the coast, infrequent in our area.

Fig. 104. *Panicum agrostoides*. Inflorescence and spikelet.

Fig. 105. *Panicum antidotale*. Plant and spikelet.

*4. PANICUM ANTIDOTALE Retz. BLUE PANICUM (Fig. 105). Stout perennial bunchgrass with primary panicles mostly 20-35 cm long and shorter secondary panicles. A native of Australia, blue panicum has been widely seeded in South Texas as a forage grass. It has become well established along roadways and in some pastures in the Coastal Bend area. Although the mature culms are firm and rather woody, this grass is rated as a fair to good forage plant.

5. PANICUM BRACHYANTHUM Steud. PIMPLE PANICUM (Fig. 106). A slender native perennial with narrow blades and wiry culms. Spikelets obovate, mostly 3-3.5 mm long. Pimple panicum is adapted to sandy soils and most frequently is present in open woodlands.

*6. PANICUM CAPILLARIOIDES Vasey. SOUTHERN WITCHGRASS (Fig. 107). Tufted native perennial with flat blades to 1 cm broad and an open panicle of narrow glabrous spikelets 5-7 mm long, these mostly at the branch tips. Second glume and sterile lemma long-prolonged beyond the tip of the caryopsis. Frequent on deep sandy and sandy loam sites, usually associated with soil disturbance or poor range condition. Of poor grazing value.

Fig. 106. *Panicum brachyantherum*. Plant, spikelet and fertile floret.

Fig. 107. *Panicum capillarioides*. Inflorescence and spikelet.

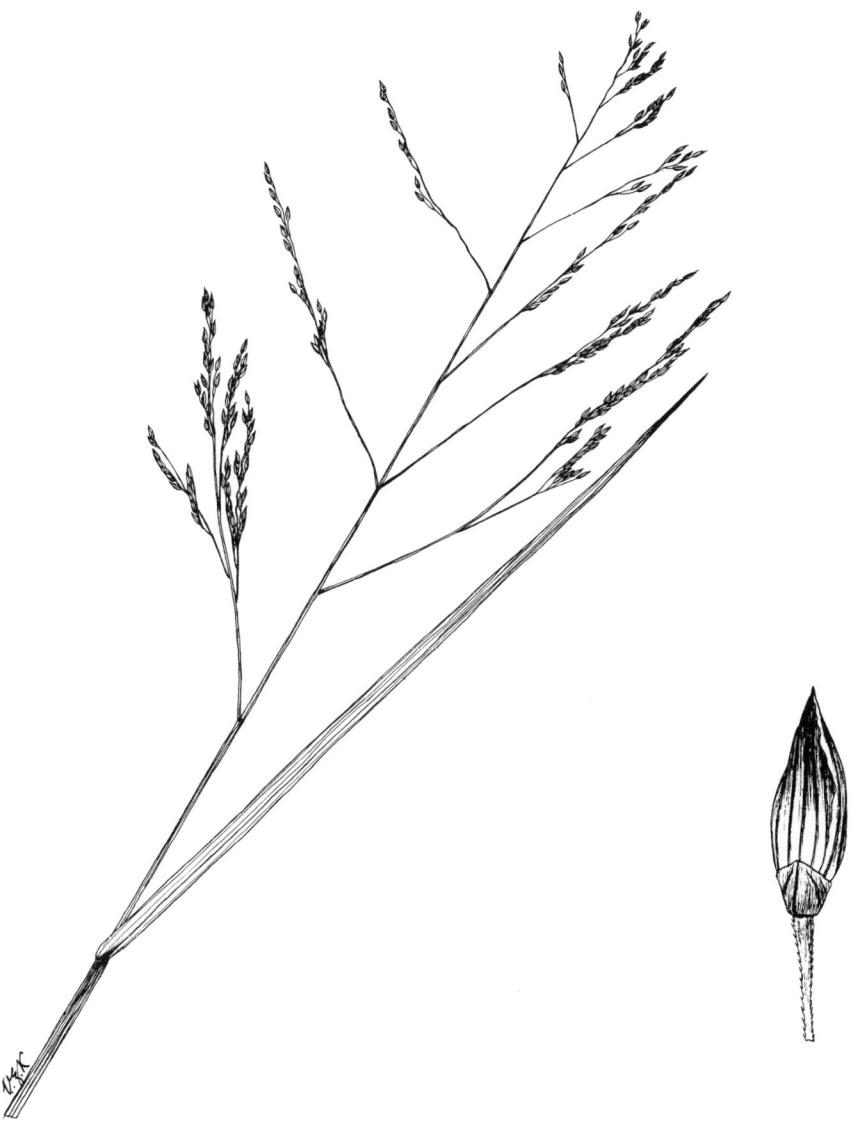

Fig. 108. *Panicum dichotomiflorum*. Inflorescence and spikelet.

*7. PANICUM DICHOTOMIFLORUM Michx. FALL PANICUM (Fig. 108). Coarse annual with thick, weak, decumbent or trailing culms often 1 to 2 meters long. Panicle large, open, bearing numerous narrow spikelets 2-3 mm long. First glume very short, obtuse or rounded at apex. Fall panicum is frequent on clay upland soils. It increases early in plant succession and may be found on overgrazed ranges in an improving condition. It is of fair forage value.

*8. PANICUM FASCICULATUM Swartz. BROWNTOP PANICUM (Fig. 109). Panicle 5-15 cm long, with few, racemose branches. Spikelets 2-3 mm long, yellowish-brown. A native warm-season annual that is locally frequent in dry lake beds and in disturbed areas on clay sites. Of poor grazing value.

*9. PANICUM FILIPES Scribn. FILLY PANICUM (Fig. 110). Tufted native perennial. Frequent on clay upland soils, often in depressions receiving extra moisture. One of the first grasses to increase on overgrazed pastures undergoing secondary succession.

Fig. 109. *Panicum fasciculatum*. Plant, spikelet and fertile floret.

Fig. 110. *Panicum filipes*. Plant and spikelet.

*10. **PANICUM GEMINATUM** Forsk. EGYPTIAN PANICUM (Fig. 111). Culms in clumps, often rooting at the lower nodes. Herbage glabrous. Ligule a fringe of hairs about 1 mm long. Native cool-season perennial. Occasional along lakes, tanks, ditches and other moist areas.

11. **PANICUM HALLII** Vasey. HALLS PANICUM (Fig. 112). Culms 15-60 cm tall, tufted. Leaves mostly in a basal clump, the blades flat, 2-6 mm broad, curling in age. Panicles 6-20 cm long, with stiffly spreading, few-flowered branches. A plant primarily adapted to dry rocky or gravely hill and valley sites, usually on limey soils. Plants on caliche sites in the northwestern portion of the Coastal Bend area appear referrable to this species.

*12. **PANICUM HIANS** Ell. GAPING PANICUM (Fig. 113). Slender native perennial. Occasional to locally frequent in sandy loam areas, especially in moist depressions. A more or less weedy plant of little forage significance.

Fig. 111. *Panicum geminatum.* Inflorescence and spikelet.

Fig. 112. *Panicum hallii*. Plant, spikelet, and fertile floret.

Fig. 113. *Panicum hians*. Plant and spikelet.

13. **PANICUM LANUGINOSUM** Ell. WOOLY PANICUM (Fig. 114). Tufted native perennial with pubescent herbage and spikelets. Culms branching in age to produce fascicles of crowded, reduced leaves and delicate few-flowered panicles. Infrequent in our area, usually in open oak woodlands.

14. **PANICUM MAXIMUM** Jacq. GUINEA GRASS. An interesting collection by F. B. Jones made in 1960 along a railroad right of way in Corpus Christi has been tentatively referred to this introduced tropical forage species. The culms of the Jones specimen are slightly over 1 meter tall and the largest panicle is about 25 cm long. The plant is referred to *P. maximum*

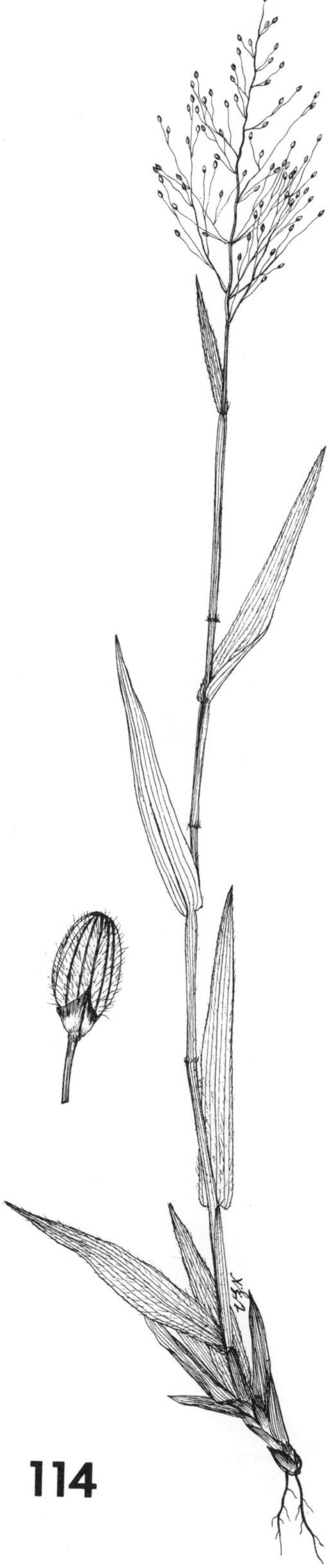

Fig. 114. *Panicum lanuginosum*. Flowering culm and spikelet.

Fig. 115. *Panicum nodatum*. Two views of spikelet (a-b) and fertile floret (c).

Fig. 116. *Panicum obtusum*. Plant and spikelet.

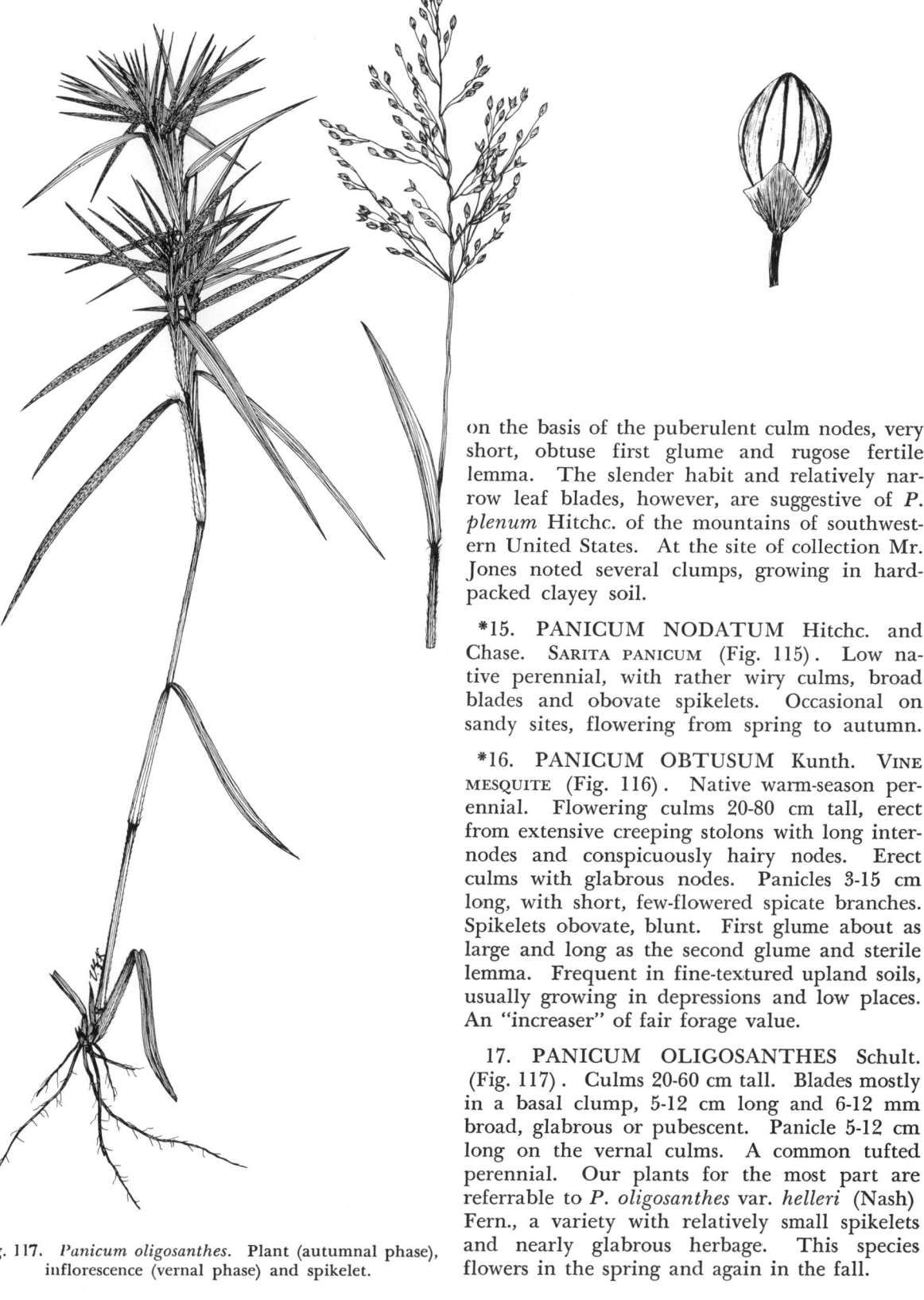

on the basis of the puberulent culm nodes, very short, obtuse first glume and rugose fertile lemma. The slender habit and relatively narrow leaf blades, however, are suggestive of *P. plenum* Hitchc. of the mountains of southwestern United States. At the site of collection Mr. Jones noted several clumps, growing in hard-packed clayey soil.

*15. PANICUM NODATUM Hitchc. and Chase. SARITA PANICUM (Fig. 115). Low native perennial, with rather wiry culms, broad blades and obovate spikelets. Occasional on sandy sites, flowering from spring to autumn.

*16. PANICUM OBTUSUM Kunth. VINE MESQUITE (Fig. 116). Native warm-season perennial. Flowering culms 20-80 cm tall, erect from extensive creeping stolons with long internodes and conspicuously hairy nodes. Erect culms with glabrous nodes. Panicles 3-15 cm long, with short, few-flowered spicate branches. Spikelets obovate, blunt. First glume about as large and long as the second glume and sterile lemma. Frequent in fine-textured upland soils, usually growing in depressions and low places. An "increaser" of fair forage value.

17. PANICUM OLIGOSANTHES Schult. (Fig. 117). Culms 20-60 cm tall. Blades mostly in a basal clump, 5-12 cm long and 6-12 mm broad, glabrous or pubescent. Panicle 5-12 cm long on the vernal culms. A common tufted perennial. Our plants for the most part are referrable to *P. oligosanthes* var. *helleri* (Nash) Fern., a variety with relatively small spikelets and nearly glabrous herbage. This species flowers in the spring and again in the fall.

Fig. 117. *Panicum oligosanthes*. Plant (autumnal phase), inflorescence (vernal phase) and spikelet.

Fig. 118. *Panicum ovinum*. Plant and spikelet.

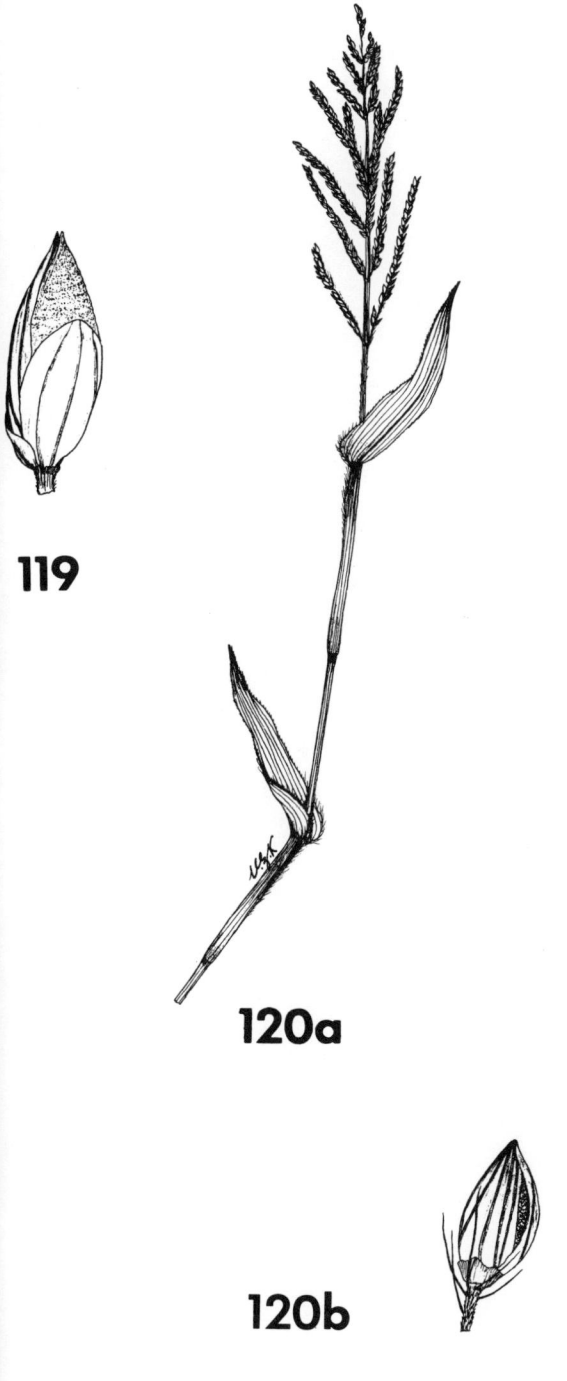

18. PANICUM OVINUM Scribn. and Smith. SHEEP PANICUM (Fig. 118). Inflorescence 5-9 cm long, with short few-flowered branches. Collected near Flour Bluff, Nueces County, in loose, sandy soil.

*19. PANICUM PALUDIVAGUM Hitchc. and Chase. WATER PANICUM (Fig. 119). Native perennial, similar to *P. geminatum* but the culms stoloniferous at the base and widely spreading. Occasional in moist sites, often in temporary water.

20. PANICUM PILCOMAYENSE Hack. Introduced perennial, collected in Matagorda and Aransas counties. This grass is generally similar to *P. filipes* but has a larger and more widely branched panicle.

21. PANICUM PORTORICENSE Desv. ex Hamilt. Low tufted native perennial, with wiry culms, broad basal blades and greatly reduced upper blades. Occasional in sandy soil, mostly in oak woodland openings.

*22. PANICUM REPTANS L. SPRAWLING PANICUM (Fig. 120). Low, weedy, native annual with decumbent, stoloniferous culms. Spikelets crowded on short, subspicate branches; pedicels bearing few long silvery, bristle-like hairs. Occasional on disturbed soils throughout the area, most frequently on heavy clay soils.

*23. PANICUM SPHAEROCARPON Ell. ROUNDSEED PANICUM (Fig. 121). Tufted native perennial with broad short blades and small panicles of nearly spherical spikelets. Flowering from spring to autumn, this grass is occasional in sandy soil, usually in open woodlands or brushy pastures.

*24. PANICUM TEXANUM Buckl. TEXAS PANICUM (Fig. 122). Coarse native annual with weak, decumbent culms, broad blades and large spikelets. Seasonally abundant on disturbed soils, Texas panicum often grows as a weed of cultivated fields, generally in sand and sandy loams. Of fair grazing value and a good producer of seeds for wildlife food.

*25. PANICUM VIRGATUM L. SWITCHGRASS (Fig. 123). Coarse bunchgrass, with culms usually 1.5-2 meters tall, in large clumps from a hard knotty rhizomatous base. Occasional on all sites but most frequent on sandy and sandy loams of valley or swale sites receiving extra moisture. A "decreaser" of good forage value.

Fig. 119. *Panicum paludivagum.* Spikelet.
Fig. 120 a-b. *Panicum reptans.* Inflorescence and spikelet.

Fig. 121. *Panicum sphaerocarpon*. Plant and spikelet.

Fig. 122. *Panicum texanum*. Inflorescence and spikelet.

Fig. 123. *Panicum virgatum*. Inflorescence, spikelet and fertile floret.

42. PAPPOPHORUM Pappusgrass

A small genus of North and South American plants, represented in the United States by two species, both of which occur in our area. These grasses have contracted spikelike panicles of bristly spikelets. The spikelets are 4-6 flowered, with only the lower 1-3 fertile. The glumes are thin and one-nerved but the lemmas are broad and many-nerved, with each nerve ending in a short awn. Disarticulation is above the glumes.

KEY TO THE SPECIES

Panicle pink or purplish-pink, narrow but usually somewhat lobed   *P. bicolor*
Panicle white or tawny, spike-like   *P. mucronulatum*

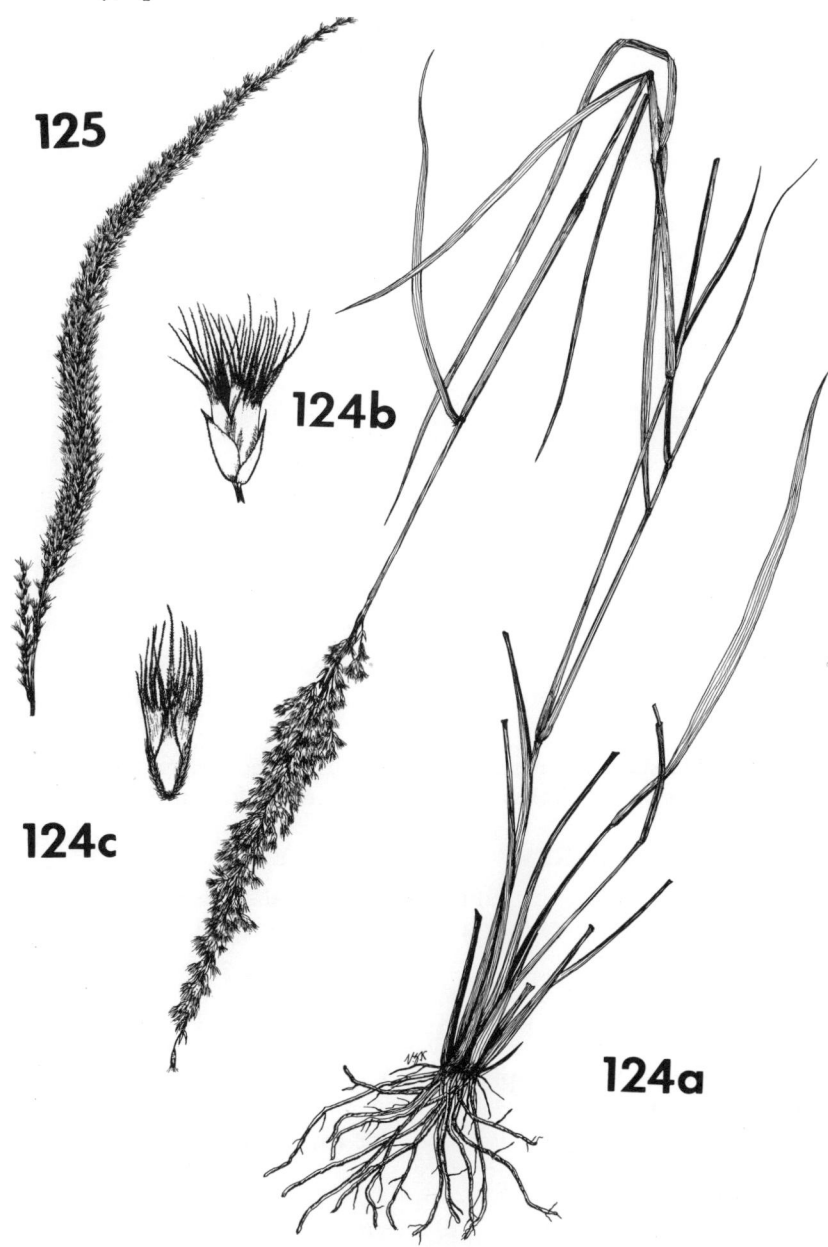

Fig. 124 a-c. *Pappophorum bicolor*. Plant (a), spikelet (b), and mature floret (c).
Fig. 125. *Pappophorum mucronulatum*. Inflorescence.

1. PAPPOPHORUM BICOLOR Fourn. PINK PAPPUSGRASS (Fig. 124). Native perennial bunchgrass, flowering from late spring to fall. Occasional on open sandy loam sites in the southern portion of our range.

2. PAPPOPHORUM MUCRONULATUM Nees. WHIPLASH PAPPUSGRASS (Fig. 125). Similar to *P. bicolor* but inflorescences more contracted and without pinkish coloration. Collected on tight calcarious soil along Corpus Christi Bay and probably of occasional occurence elsewhere in the southwestern portion of our area.

43. PARAPHOLIS

Tufted annual with cylindrical spikes. Spikelets solitary at the nodes, embedded in the rachis and falling attached to the rachis joint. Glumes firm, pointed, placed in front of the spikelet.

1. PARAPHOLIS INCURVA (L.) C. E. Hubb. SICKLEGRASS (Fig. 126). Adventative warm-season annual, native of Europe. Although only recently reported for Texas (Gould, 1955) this weedy annual is now known to be locally abundant in sandy saline sites at several localities along the coast. It commonly is associated with *Spartina* and *Distichlis* along ditches and coastal flats.

Fig. 126. *Parapholis incurva*. Plant and spikelet with section of rachis.

44. PASPALUM

Inflorescence of one to many spicate branches, these racemose or occasionally paired at the culm apex. Spikelets plano-convex, broad, awnless. First glume usually absent (vestigial in a few species).

A genus of some 200 species, present in the warm and warm-temperate regions of the world. The 34 species present in Texas are all warm-season perennials.

KEY TO THE SPECIES

Inflorescence branches two, paired at the culm apex (less than 1 cm apart)
  Spikelets broadly ovate or oblong, obtuse at the apex; plants of prairies and woodlands
    Spikelets 2.5 mm or less long   *P. minus*
    Spikelets 3-3.5 mm long   *P. notatum*
  Spikelets narrowly ovate or oblong, tapering to an acute apex; plants of coastal saline flats and marshes
    Second glume minutely pubescent; spikelets 2.5-3.5 mm long   *P. distichum*
    Second glume glabrous; spikelets 3.5-4 mm long   *P. vaginiflorum*
Inflorescence branches one to several, if two then 1-2 cm or more apart
  Inflorescence branches typically 10-20 or more
    First glume present; spikelet glabrous   (*Panicum geminatum*)
    First glume absent; spikelet ciliate or pubescent
      Spikelet acute at apex, ciliate with long hairs along margins to base.   *P. urvillei*
      Spikelet obtuse at apex, pubescent only at or near the tip   *P. virgatum*
  Inflorescence branches 6 (rarely 8) or less

First glume present on at least some of the spikelets; spikelets narrowly oblong.   A.
First glums absent on all spikelets   AA.

A.

Spikelets pubescent; plants without rhizomes   *P. langei*
Spikelets glabrous; plants developing stout rhizomes; inflorescence a single slender raceme or of 2 racemose branches
  Blades flat, 8-15 mm broad   *P. unispicatum*
  Blades involute, 5 mm or less broad   *P. monostachyum*

AA.

Spikelets long-ciliate on the margins, acute at the apex   *P. dilatatum*
Spikelets glabrous or puberulent but not long-ciliate
  Spikelets about 4 mm long   *P. floridanum*
  Spikelets less than 3.5 mm long
    Spikelets suborbicular
      Spikelets mostly 1.4-2.2 mm long   *P. setaceum*
      Spikelets 2.6-3.2 mm long   *P. laeve* var. *circulare*
    Spikelets ovate or oblong
      Fertile lemma and palea dark brown at maturity; culms erect at base, often in large clumps   *P. plicatulum*
      Fertile lemma and palea not dark brown at maturity; culms decumbent or trailing at base, not developed in large clumps
        Spikelets glabrous, 2-2.5 mm long; inflorescence branches mostly 3 cm or less long, with a broad, flat rachis   *P. lividum*
        Spikelets puberulent (rarely glabrous), 3-3.5 mm long; inflorescence branches mostly more than 3 cm long
          Leaves mostly 6-15 mm broad, lanceolate; spikelets obovate, turgidly plano-convex   *P. pubiflorum*
          Leaves mostly 2-6 mm broad, linear; spikelets elliptic, depressed plano-convex   *P. hartwegianum*

1. **PASPALUM DILATATUM** Poir. DALLISGRASS (Fig. 127). Introduced warm-season perennial. Seeded as a pasture grass in many area, dallisgrass occurs in the Coastal Bend area as an occasional weed of roadsides and other disturbed sites. It is best adapted to clay soils.

2. **PASPALUM DISTICHUM** L. KNOTGRASS (Fig. 128). Plants developing decumbent stoloniferous culms and usually rhizomes. Native warm-season perennial, growing mostly along the margins of fresh water ditches and ponds, occasional in saline areas.

3. **PASPALUM FLORIDANUM** Michx. FLORIDA PASPALUM (Fig. 129). Tall, rather coarse native bunchgrass with large spikelets. The typical form has more or less pubescent herbage. Plants with glabrous herbage have been recognized as var. *glabratum* Englem. but this variant does not appear worthy of formal recognition. Florida paspalum is infrequent in our area. It grows mainly in sandy woods openings.

*4. **PASPALUM HARTWEGIANUM** Fourn. HARTWEG PASPALUM (Fig. 130). Native perennial bunchgrass, similar in general aspect to *P. pubiflorum* but base of plant less firm and knotty, the leaf blades narrower, the inflorescence branches tending to be erect rather than spreading at maturity, and the spikelets slightly smaller (3 mm long) and neatly compressed together. In *P. pubiflorum* the spikelets are more turgid, somewhat broader and usually less regularly arranged on the branches. Hartweg paspalum is much less frequent in our area than is *P. pubiflorum*.

5. **PASPALUM LAEVE** Michx. var. *circulare* (Nash) Stone. ROUNDSEED PASPALUM. Native perennial bunchgrass, known in the Coastal Bend area from a single collection made near Corpus Christi.

*6. **PASPALUM LANGEI** (Fourn.) Nash. RUSTYSEED PASPALUM (Fig. 131). Inflorescence branches 2-5, mostly 4-10 cm long, bearing more or less paired spikelets. Spikelets 2.2-2.6 mm long, pubescent, blotched or speckled. Second spikelet of a pair with a well-developed glume. Occasional in sandy woods openings, usually in partial shade.

Fig 127. *Paspalum dilatatum*. Inflorescence and spikelet. Fig. 128. *Paspalum distichum*. Inflorescence and spikelet.

Fig. 129. *Paspalum floridanum*. Plant, spikelet and fertile floret.

Fig. 130. *Paspalum hartwegianum.* Spikelet.
Fig. 131 a-b. *Paspalum langei.* Inflorescence and pair of spikelets.

Fig. 132. *Paspalum lividum*. Plant and spikelet.

*7. **PASPALUM LIVIDUM** Trin. LONG-TOM (Fig. 132). Native perennial, with decumbent, creeping culms as much as 6 feet or more in length. Occasional in ditches and along streams and marshes.

8. **PASPALUM MINUS** Fourn. MAT PASPALUM. Plants low, creeping commonly developing dense mats. This native perennial is similar to the introduced *P. notatum* but has more slender culms and inflorescence branches, and smaller spikelets. Growing primarily on open prairies, mat paspalum is reported by Jones *et al.* (1961) from Aransas County.

*9. **PASPALUM MONOSTACHYUM** Vasey. GULFDUNE PASPALUM (Fig. 133). Culms one to few at the nodes of extensive creeping rhizomes. Spikelets 3-3.5 mm long, some with irregularly developed first glumes. Native perennial, occasional on coastal dunes and in sandy sites along coastal woodlands.

*10 **PASPALUM NOTATUM** Flugge. BAHIAGRASS (Fig. 134). Culms 20-50 cm tall, from hard, decumbent more or less sod-forming bases. Native to Mexico, Central and South America, this grass is well established in southern United States on sandy and sandy loam soils, often in partial shade.

*11. **PASPALUM PLICATULUM** Michx. BROWNSEED PASPALUM (Fig. 135). Native perennial bunchgrass with rather stiffly erect culms 50-100 cm tall. Blades mostly 4-6 mm broad and 20-35 cm long, glabrous or with a few long hairs near the ligule. Ligule a glabrous membrane 2-3 mm long. Inflorescence with usually 3-8 branches, these mostly 3-8 cm long. Spikelets mostly 2.5-2.8 mm long. Glume and sterile lemma glabrous or slightly puberulent. Frequent in sandy soils of prairies and open woodlands and "increaser" of fair forage value.

*12. **PASPALUM PUBIFLORUM** Rupr. and Fourn. HAIRYSEED PASPALUM (Fig. 136). Culms 40-100 cm tall, decumbent at the base. Blades broad, glabrous except for a few hairs near the base. Very similar to *P. hartwegianum*, differing in the characters discussed under the species. Frequent in our area on clay soils along ditches, oak motts, and other areas of moist heavy soils.

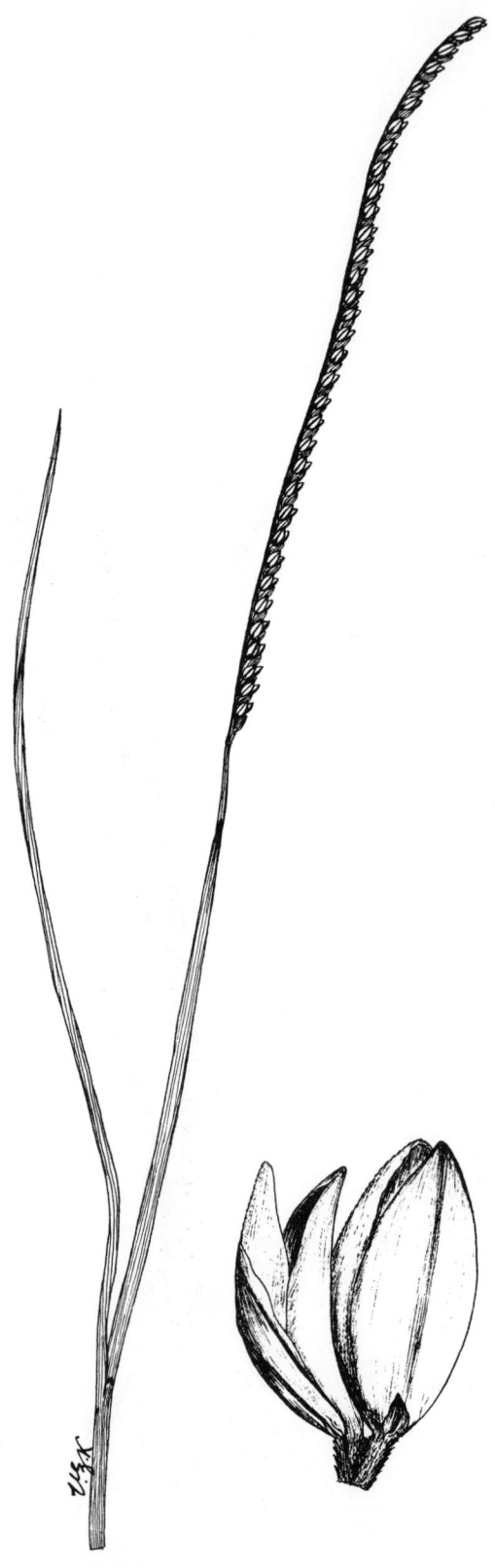

Fig. 133. *Paspalum monostachyum.* Inflorescence and spikelet.

Fig. 134. *Paspalum notatum*. Inflorescence.
Fig. 135 a-b. *Paspalum plicatulum*. Inflorescence and pair of spikelets.

Fig. 136. *Paspalum pubiflorum*. Inflorescence and pair of spikelets.

*13. **PASPALUM SETACEUM** Michx. *(P. ciliatifolium* Michx.; *P. muhlenbergii* Nash; *P. stramineum* Nash) THIN PASPALUM (Fig. 137). Low, short-lived tufted native perennial. Leaves nearly glabrous to variously pubescent. Blades flat, bright green, mostly 6-12 mm or more broad. Ligule a minute, lacerated membrane bordered by a dense fringe of stiff hairs. Inflorescence a single spicate raceme or with 2-3 slender racemose branches. Spikelets glabrous to puberulent.

The grouping of plants previously referred to *P. setaceum, P. ciliatifolium, P. muhlenbergii* and *P. stramineum* in a single species is in accordance with the concept of Banks (1963). Banks proposes to recognize two varieties of *P. setaceum* in our area, one based on plants of the *P. stramineum* type and the other based on plants of the *P. muhlenbergii* type. The new name combinations have not been published. According to Banks (personal communication), the former variety, with leaves that are almost glabrous or pilose but that nearly always are somewhat puberulent on the upper surface near the tip, and usually veinless sterile lemmas, is the common type in our area. A few collections of *P. muhlenbergii* type plants, with usually pilose but not puberulent leaves and sterile lemmas that are usually veined, have been made in the Coastal Bend area.

14. **PASPALUM UNISPICATUM** (Scribn. and Merr.) Nash. ONESPIKE PASPALUM. Culms arising singly or in small clumps at the nodes of a stout rhizome. Leaf blades flat, rather stiff, more or less papillose-hairy. Inflorescence usually a single long slender raceme of narrowly oblong spikelets 3-3.3 mm long. Known in our area only from near Kingsville, this species ranges from South Texas through Central and South America.

15. **PASPALUM URVILLEI** Steud. VASEYGRASS (Fig. 138). Large coarse bunchgrass, with numerous stiffly erect culms. Spikelets small, conspicuously pubescent, numerous in a large inflorescence with many racemose branches. Sandy ditches, swales and other areas of moist disturbed soils. Native to South America but becoming abundant in southern United States, including southeastern Texas. Infrequent in our area.

Fig. 137. *Paspalum setaceum*. Inflorescence and spikelet.

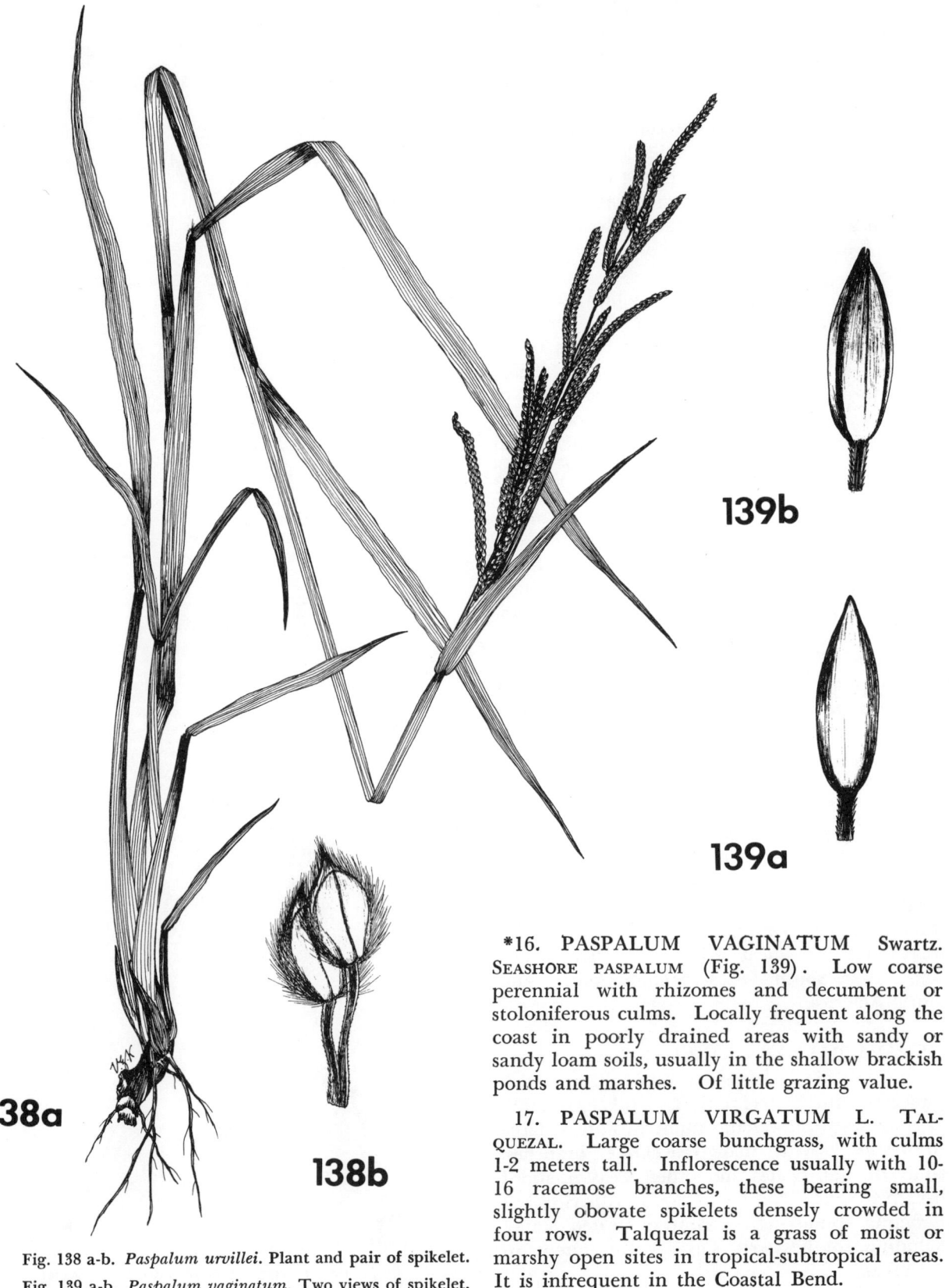

*16. **PASPALUM VAGINATUM** Swartz. SEASHORE PASPALUM (Fig. 139). Low coarse perennial with rhizomes and decumbent or stoloniferous culms. Locally frequent along the coast in poorly drained areas with sandy or sandy loam soils, usually in the shallow brackish ponds and marshes. Of little grazing value.

17. **PASPALUM VIRGATUM** L. TAL-QUEZAL. Large coarse bunchgrass, with culms 1-2 meters tall. Inflorescence usually with 10-16 racemose branches, these bearing small, slightly obovate spikelets densely crowded in four rows. Talquezal is a grass of moist or marshy open sites in tropical-subtropical areas. It is infrequent in the Coastal Bend.

Fig. 138 a-b. *Paspalum urvillei*. Plant and pair of spikelet.
Fig. 139 a-b. *Paspalum vaginatum*. Two views of spikelet.

45. PHALARIS Canarygrass

Inflorescence a contracted spike-like panicle. Spikelets with a single fertile floret and 1-2 scale-like rudiments below. Lemma and glumes awnless, the latter large, subequal and usually winged on the midnerve.

A small genus of grasses of temperate and cool-temperate regions of Europe and North America. The six species that occur in Texas all are cool-season plants and all but one are annual.

KEY TO THE SPECIES

Fertile lemma 4.5-6 mm long; panicle mostly 3 cm or less long, usually half or more as broad as long; keel of glumes with a wing 1 mm or slightly less broad *P. canariensis*

Fertile lemma 3-4 mm long, panicle usually more than 3 cm long but less on depauperate plants, less than half as broad as long; keel of glume wing mostly 0.5 mm or less broad *P. carolinana*

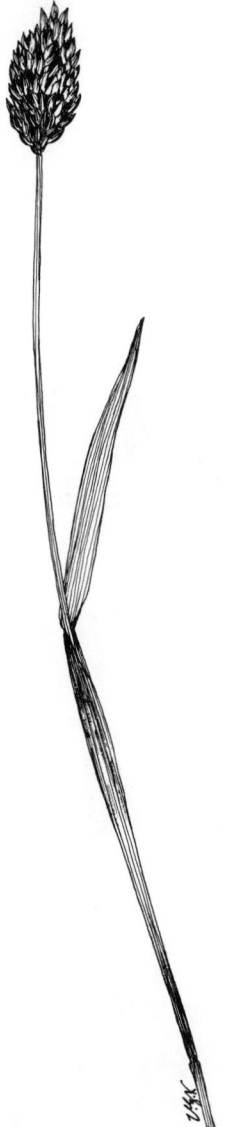

*1. PHALARIS CANARIENSIS L. CANARY-GRASS (Fig. 140). Introduced annual, growing in the spring as an adventative weed and usually not persisting in an area. This is a common constituent of bird-seed mixes and the occasional occurrence of the plant in our area probably results from the feeding of the seeds to canaries and other pet birds.

*2. P H A L A R I S CAROLINIANA Walt. CAROLINIA CANARYGRASS (Fig. 141). Low succulent native annual. Occasional to abundant in early spring in wet, poorly drained areas, usually on disturbed soils. Of poor grazing value.

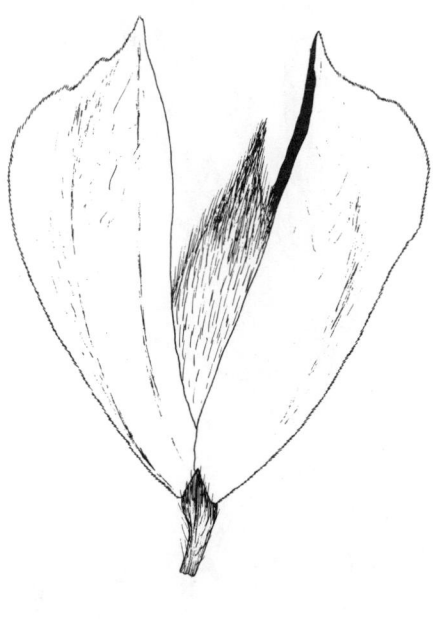

Fig. 140. *Phalaris canariensis.* Inflorescence and spikelet.

Fig. 141. *Phalaris caroliniana.* Plant, spikelet, and fertile floret with rudiments at its base.

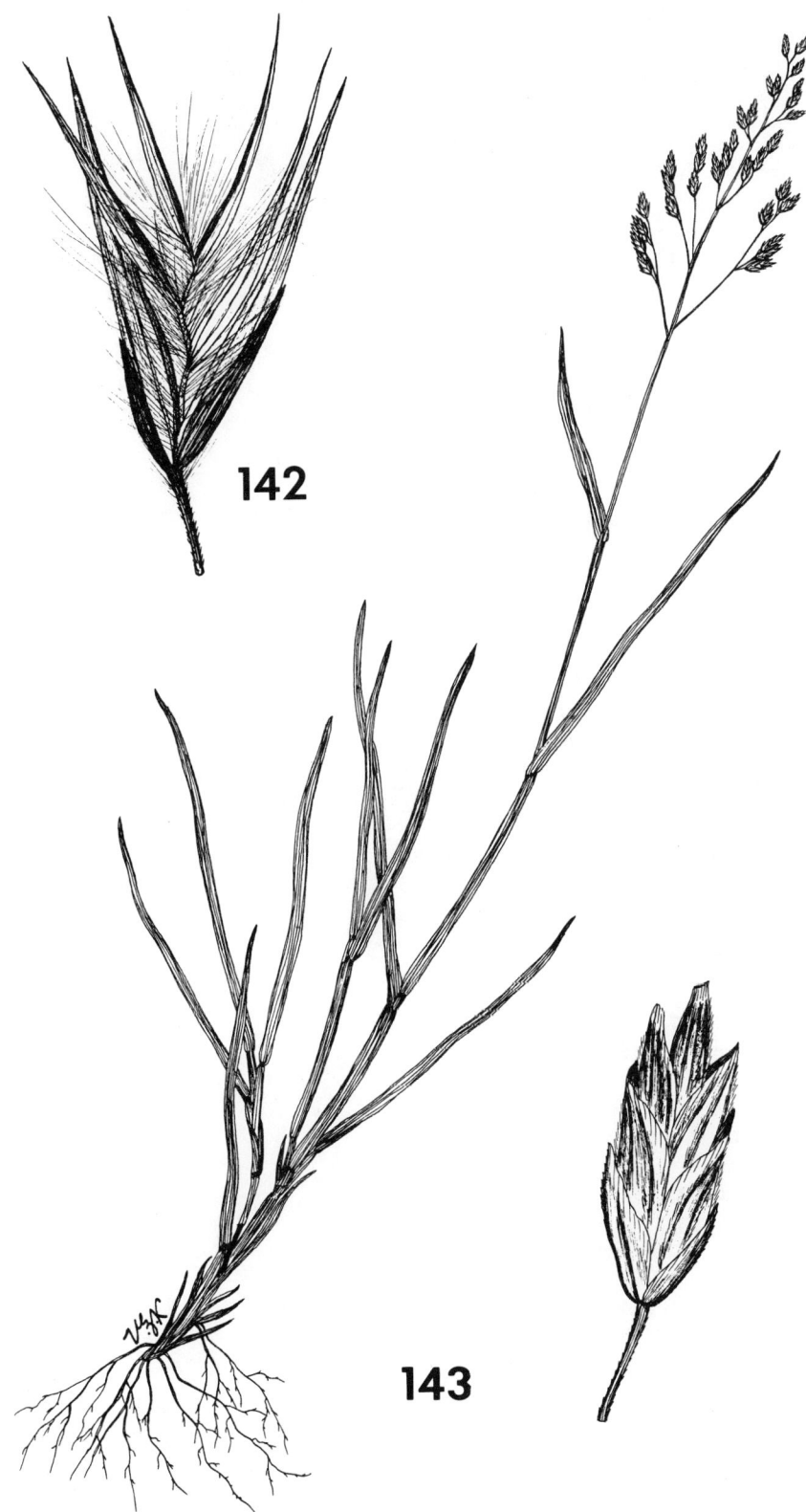

Fig. 142. *Phragmites communis*. Spikelet.

Fig. 143. *Poa annua*. Plant and spikelet.

46. PHRAGMITES

Tall perennials, with rhizomes and stout culms. Species 3, one in Asia, one in Argentina and one throughout the temperate and warm regions of the world.

*1. PHRAGMITES COMMUNIS Trin. COMMON REED (Fig. 142). Introduced warm-season perennial with culms 2-3 meters or more tall and large paniculate inflorescences. Occasional to locally abundant along streams, ditches and other moist sites, often in shallow water.

47. POA Bluegrass

A genus of about 200 species, these mostly in temperate and subartic regions. Many of these grasses are important forage plants and others are highly valued as turf grasses.

1. POA ANNUA L. ANNUAL BLUEGRASS (Fig. 143). Low-tufted cool-season annual, with open panicles. Occasional in our area as a weed of lawns, roadsides and other disturbed sites in late winter and early spring. Adventative from Europe, now established as a casual weed throughout North America.

48. POLYPOGON

Annuals and weak perennials with dense irregularly lobed panicles of small spikelets. Spikelets one-flowered, disarticulating below the glumes. Glumes about equal, abruptly awned, exceeding the lemma in length. A genus of about 10 species, these mainly in temperate regions of Europe and Asia. Only one species, *P. elongatus* H.B.K., is native to the United States.

1. POLYPOGON MONSPELIENSIS (L.) Desf. RABBITFOOT GRASS (Fig. 144). Plants with usually weak, geniculate culms, these often rooting at the lower nodes. Panicles dense, light green, those of our plants relatively large for this species.

This adventative cool-season annual grows as a weed along streams, ditches and swales. It occurs in areas of high salinity as well as along bodies of fresh water.

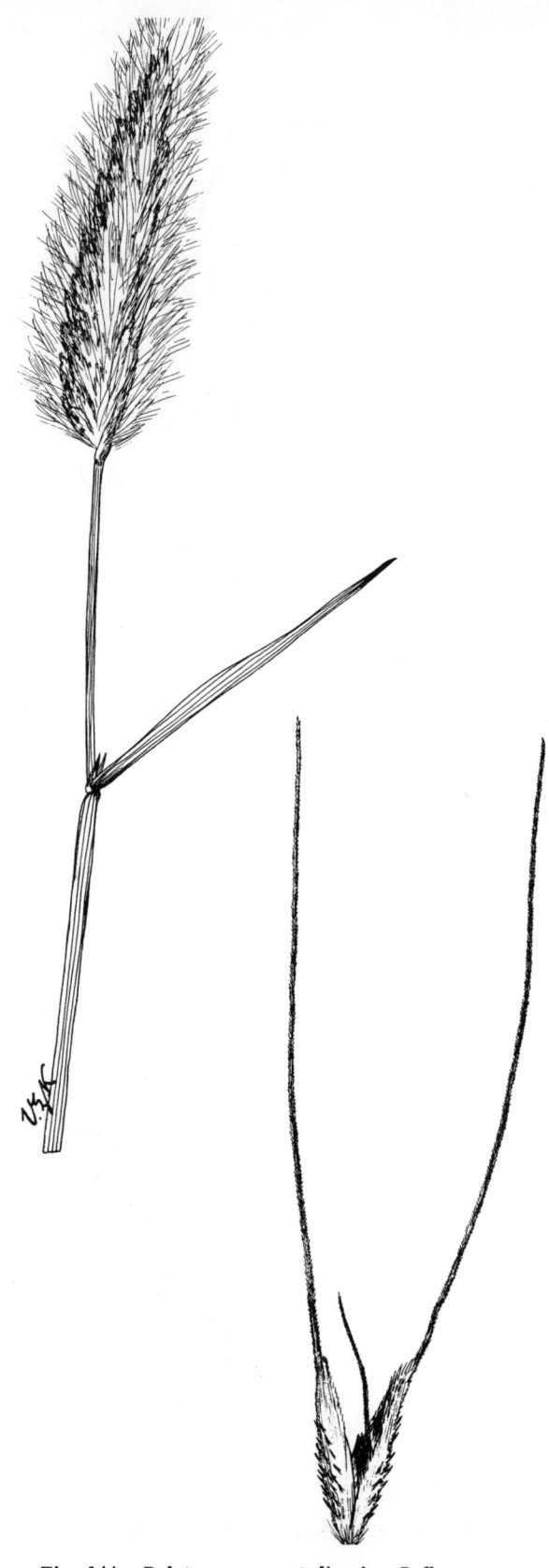

Fig. 144. *Polypogon monspeliensis.* Inflorescence and spikelet.

49. SCHEDONNARDUS

A genus of one species, this growing on the plains and prairies of central and southern United States and also present in Argentina.

*1. SCHEDONNARDUS PANICULATUS (Nutt.) Trel. TUMBLEGRASS (Fig. 145). Low-tufted perennial with wiry culms. Inflorescence much exceeding the leafy portion of the plant, with slender, stiffly curved branches bearing widely spaced but closely appressed spikelets. At maturity the inflorescence breaks off at the base and becomes a tumbleweed. This native warm-season grass is frequent in heavily grazed pastures on clay upland sites, often associated with *Bouteloua rigidiseta*, *Aristidia* species and other "poor quality" forage plants. Tumblegrass, itself, is of low forage value.

50. SCLEROPOA

A genus of one species, this native to southern Europe. Reported as a weedy adventative in scattered localities in the United States.

1. SCLEROPOA RIGIDA (L.) Griseb. STIFFGRASS (Fig. 146). Low, tufted, warm-season annual. Culms slender, erect, 15-45 cm tall. Herbage glabrous. Ligule membranous, 1.5-2.0 mm long. Blades thin, flat or folded, 1-4 mm broad. Inflorescence 3-10 cm long, the spikelets on short, stout pedicels, either in a spicate raceme or on short lateral branches as well as on the main axis. Spikelets glabrous, awnless, mostly 4-7 flowered. Glumes thick, subequal, slightly shorter than the lemmas. Lemmas about 2 mm long, rounded on the back.

Known in the Coastal Bend region by a single collection, made by V. L. Cory in 1945 on dunes of the Aransas Wildlife Refuge, Aransas County.

Fig. 145. *Schedonnardus paniculatus*. Inflorescence and spikelet.

51. SETARIA Bristlegrass

Inflorescence a contracted, usually spike-like panicle. Spikelets, at least in part, subtended by one to several bristles, these representing reduced branchlets. Spikelets deciduous as a whole (except in the cultivated *S. italica*), disarticulating above the bristles, leaving a discoid or cup-shaped callus. Spikelets essentially similar to those of *Panicum*. A group of about 75 species, both annuals and perennials, widely distributed in temperate and tropical regions of the world. In Texas the species of *Setaria* grow as warm-season plants. Reference should be made here to the recently published monographic treatment of the genus *Setaria* in North America (Rominger, 1962).

Fig. 146. *Scleropoa rigida*. Plant and spikelet.

KEY TO THE SPECIES

Bristles 4-12 below each spikelet; fertile lemma coarsely transverse-rugose

    Plants annual, the culms and culm bases not hard and wiry; leaf blades with a loose spiral twist *S. glauca*

    Plants perennial, with hard culm bases and usually short knotty rhizomes; blades without a spiral twist *S. geniculata*

Bristles 1-3 below each spikelet

    Bristles mostly below only the uppermost spikelet of each branchlet; fertile lemma moderately transverse-rugose

        Culms from a hard, knotty, rhizomatous base; leaf blades usually 12 cm or less long, not narrowed towards the base

            Mid-culm blades 2-3 (rarely-4) mm broad, gradually tapering to the apex; inflorescence bristles usually not longer than the spikelets *S. ramiseta*

            Mid-culm blades, at least some, 4.5-8.0 mm broad, abruptly narrowing to the apex; bristles usually longer than the spikelets *S. firmula*

        Culm densely tufted, the bases firm but not rhizomatous; leaf blades usually 13-20 cm long and 2.5-4 (rarely 5) mm broad, narrowed towards the base *S. reverchoni*

    Bristles usually present below all spikelets; fertile lemma smooth, minutely reticulate or moderately rugose

        Plants annual

            Bristles retrorsely scabrous, at least in part; inflorescence cylindric, 5-10 mm wide. *S. adhaerans*

            Bristles antrorsely scabrous; inflorescence lobed, to 3 cm wide; cultivated species *S. italica*

        Plants perennial

            Panicles 3-6 (-8) cm long; culms often branching above; spikelets 1.9-2.1 mm long *S. texana*

            Panicles 8-20 cm or more long; spikelets more than 2.1 mm long

                Palea of sterile floret nearly as long as palea of fertile floret; palea of fertile floret slightly to strongly convex; lemma of mature fertile floret inflated at base *S. macrostachya*

                Palea of sterile floret usually less than three-fourths as long as palea of fertile floret; palea of fertile floret flat or concave; lemma of fertile floret not inflated at base

                    Blades 4-9 mm wide, flat or folded, rarely pubescent; panicle usually columnar; bristles usually appressed, 5-12 mm long; culms mostly stiffly erect, infrequently geniculate *S. leucopila*

                    Blades 9-20 mm wide, flat, commonly pubescent; panicle usually tapering from base to apex; bristles spreading, 10-35 mm long; culms usually geniculate *S. scheelei*

1. SETARIA ADHAERANS (Forsskal) Chiovenda. (Fig. 147). Weedy adventative annual, with usually numerous genticulate-spreading culms. Infrequent in our area, collected as a wayside weed in Corpus Christi.

*2. SETARIA FIRMULA (Hitchc. & Chase) Pilger. *(Panicum fimulum* Hitchc. and Chase). (Fig. 148). Native warm-season perennial. Culms mostly 25-40 cm tall, stiffly erect from a firm base. Ligule a ring of hairs 1.5-2.0 mm long. Inflorescence contracted, few-flowered, with bristles developed only below spikelets terminating the short, appressed branchlets. Spikelets mostly 3.0-3.2 mm long. Frequent on deep sandy soils, usually in heavily grazed areas of open prairie. Often associated with *Brachiaria ciliatissima* and difficult to distinguish from this grass. vegetatively.

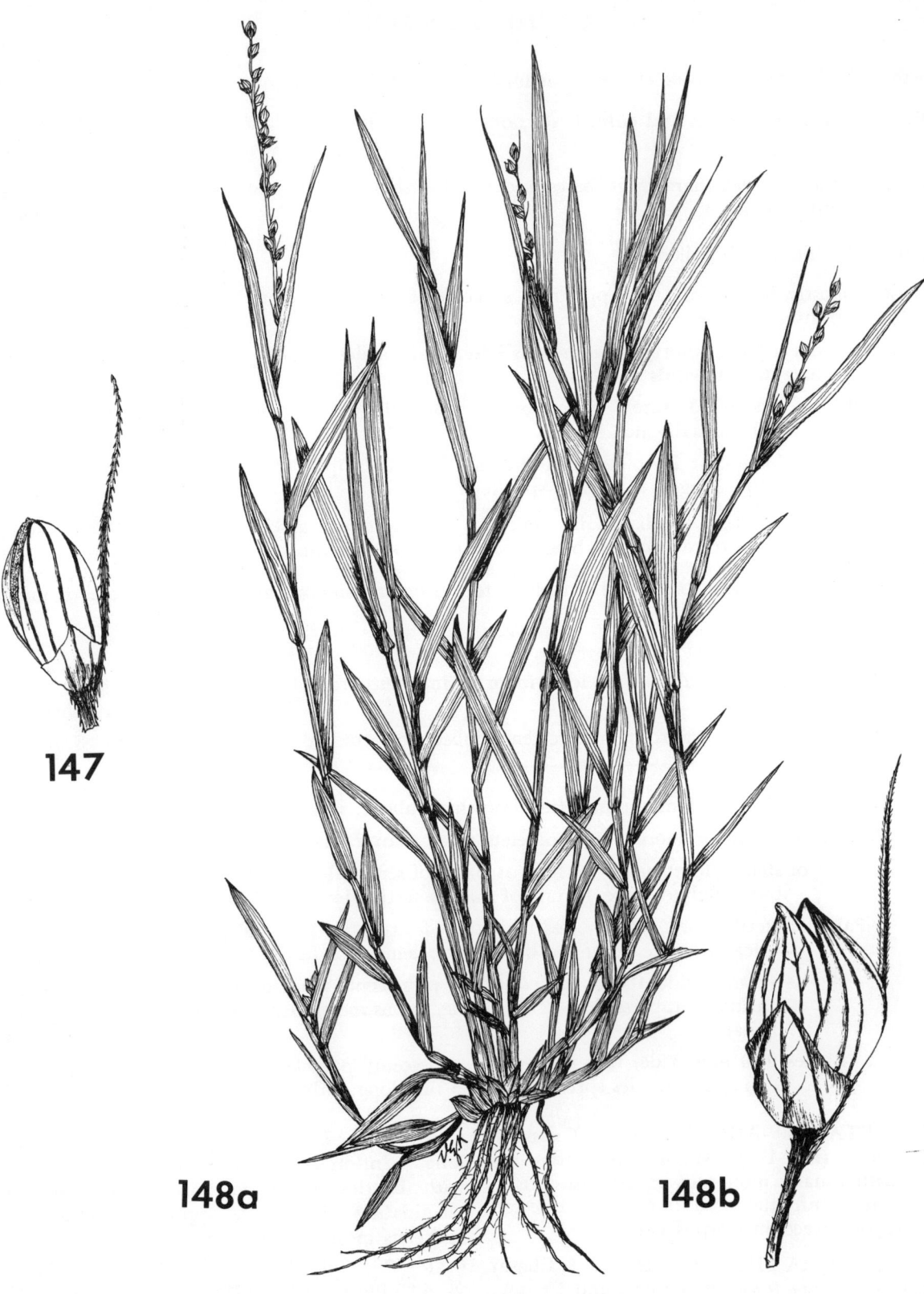

Fig. 147. *Setaria adhaerans*. Spikelet.
Fig. 148 a-b. *Setaria firmula*. Plant and spikelet.

*3. SETARIA GENICULATA (Lam.) Beauv. KNOTROOT BRISTLEGRASS (Fig. 149). Native perennial, usually 30-60 cm tall, with culms stiffly erect from a firm, knotty base, often with short rhizomes. Blades flat, mostly 4-7 mm broad. Inflorescence cylindrical, spikelike. Spikelets 2.0-2.8 mm long. Both glumes shorter than the sterile lemma, the first slightly less than half as long, the second slightly more than half as long. This native perennial is frequent and somewhat weedy in loam and clay soils, epecially in areas of poor drainage. It is of fair forage value but seldom grows in sufficient stand to be of significance as a forage grass.

4. SETARIA GLAUCA (L.) Beauv. *(S. lutescens* sensu Hubbard). YELLOW BRISTLEGRASS. Inflorescence cylindrical, densely contracted. Spikelets mostly 3.0-3.5 mm long. Fertile lemma conspicuously rugose. An adventative annual weed of roadsides and waste places, flowering from late spring throughout the summer. Not known definitely to occur in the Coastal Bend area but to be expected.

5. SETARIA ITALICA (I). Beauv. FOXTAIL MILLET. A cultivated annual of diverse habit and many commercial strains. Typically the panicle are large, dense and lobed, often as much as 30 cm long and 3 cm thick. Spikelet color and awn length are variable. This species is reported by Jones *et al.* (1961) to occur in the Coastal Bend area.

*6. SETARIA LEUCOPILA (Scribn. and Merr.) K. Schum. PLAINS BRISTLEGRASS (Fig. 150). Culms mostly 40-120 cm tall, stiffly erect, in large or small clumps. Panicle cylindrical, tightly contracted and spike-like. This native perennial includes for the most part those plants of the United States referred to *S. macrostachya* H.B.K. in Hitchcock's Manual (1950). Plains bristlegrass is locally abundant in prairie associations on clay and clay loam sites. Of good forage value, it is a part of the early successional stages of vegetation following disturbance.

7. SETARIA MACROSTACHYA H.B.K. Perennial bunchgrass with stout, tall culms and thick, densely-flowered spicate panicles 1-2 cm in diameter. Bristles 10-20 mm long, usually solitary below each spikelet. Most plants of the United States previously referred to this species are now included in the *S. leucopila* taxon. *Setaria macrostachya* is limited in its distribution to Mexico, southern Texas and southern Arizona.

*8. SETARIA RAMISETA (Scribn.) Pilger. (*Panicum ramisetum* Scribn.). (Fig. 151). Low tufted native perennial, with contracted, few-flowered spikelike panicles or racemes mostly 3-8 cm long. Spikelets mostly 2.4-2.8 mm long. Occasional on sandy soils throughout the area.

Fig. 149. *Setaria geniculata.* Inflorescence and spikelet.

Fig. 150. *Setaria leucopila*. Plant and spikelet.

Fig. 151. *Setaria ramiseta*. Plant and spikelet.

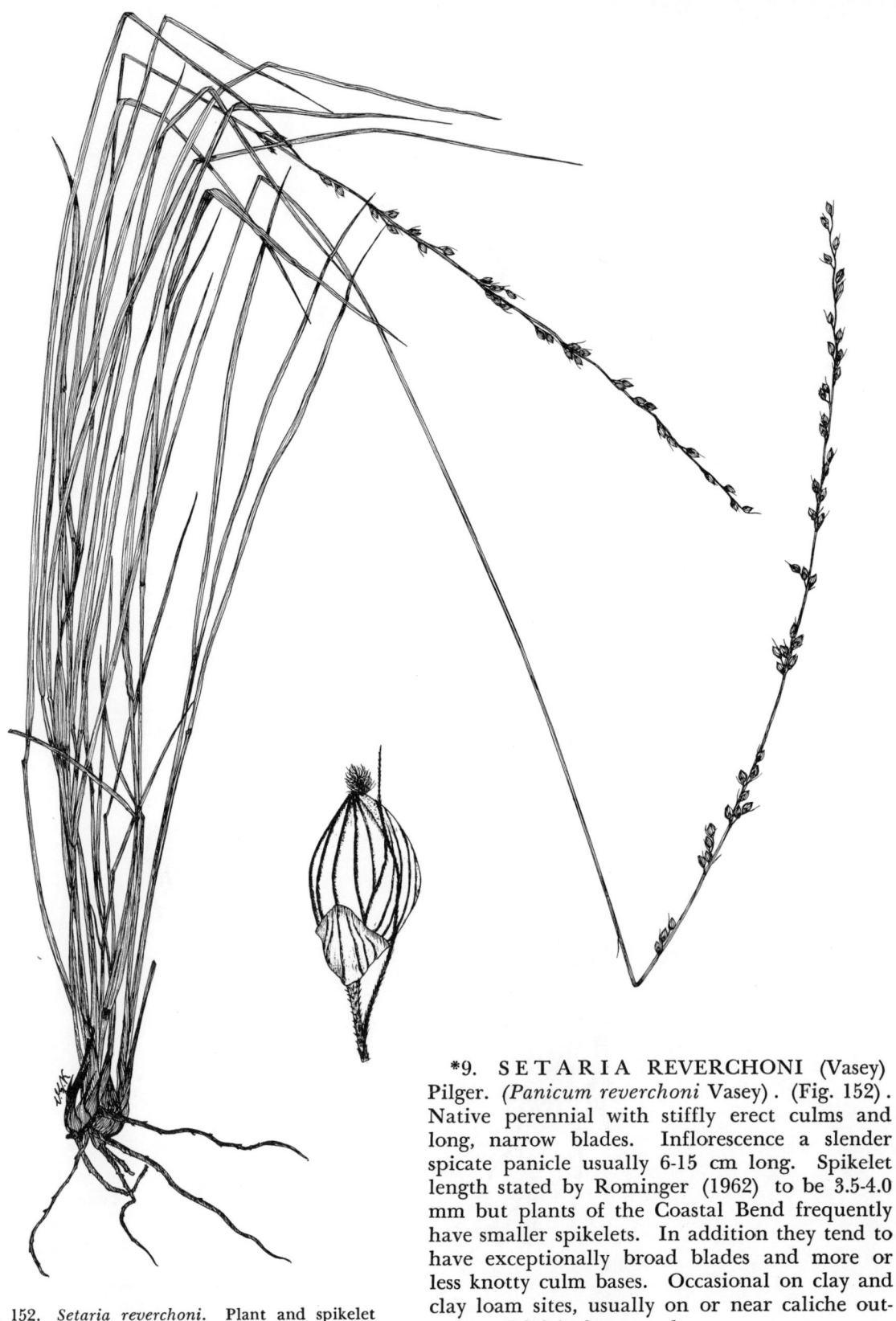

Fig. 152. *Setaria reverchoni.* Plant and spikelet subtended by bristle.

*9. SETARIA REVERCHONI (Vasey) Pilger. *(Panicum reverchoni* Vasey). (Fig. 152). Native perennial with stiffly erect culms and long, narrow blades. Inflorescence a slender spicate panicle usually 6-15 cm long. Spikelet length stated by Rominger (1962) to be 3.5-4.0 mm but plants of the Coastal Bend frequently have smaller spikelets. In addition they tend to have exceptionally broad blades and more or less knotty culm bases. Occasional on clay and clay loam sites, usually on or near caliche outcrops. Of fair forage value.

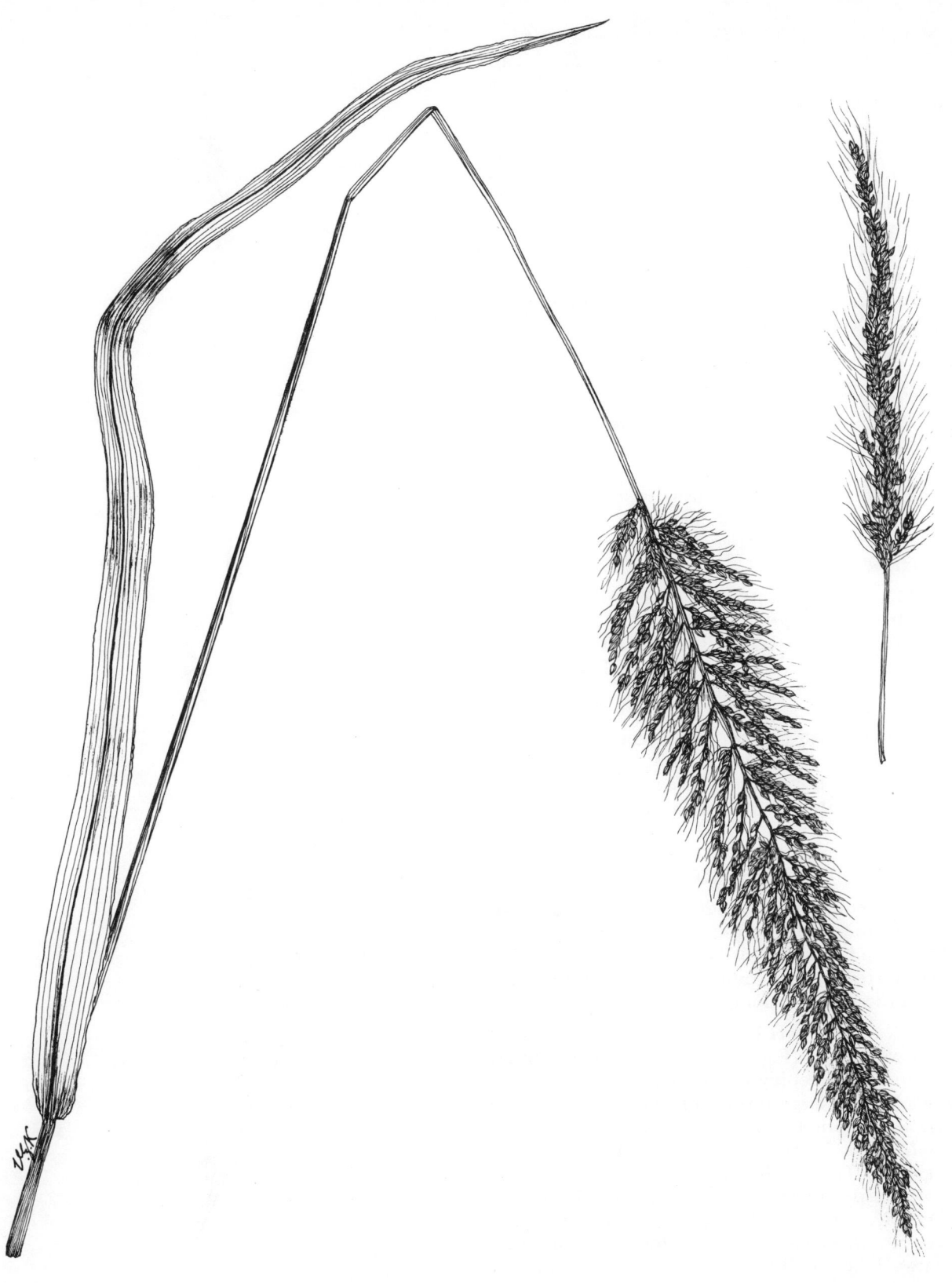

Fig. 153. *Setaria scheelei*. Two types of panicles.

*10. **SETARIA SCHEELEI** (Steud.) Hitchc. SOUTHWESTERN BRISTLEGRASS (Fig. 153). Tall coarse perennial with culms usually 50-100 cm long, broad leaf blades, and large rather loose, panicles. Frequent in our area, mostly in sandy loam soils and usually in the shade of trees or shrubs. This grass provides excellent forage and also produces a good crop of seed for wildlife food.

*11. **SETARIA TEXANA** Emery. TEXAS BRISTLEGRASS (Fig. 154). Low, tufted perennial, with narrow blades and short, few-flowered panicles. Occasional on loamy soils, usually in the shade of trees or shrubs.

52. SORGHASTRUM Indiangrass

Tall perennials with broad flat blades and loosely contracted panicles. Spikelets basically in pairs of one sessile and one pedicelled but the pedicelled spikelet usually completely reduced and represented by the pedicel alone. Species about 10, native to the warmer parts of both hemispheres.

*1. **SORGHASTRUM NUTANS** (L.) Nash. YELLOW INDIANGRASS (Fig. 155). Culms mostly 1-2 meters tall, stiffly erect from stout rhizomes. Panicles contracted, yellowish, 15-30 cm long. Branchlets, rachis joints, pedicels and spikelets hirsute. Sessile spikelet usually 6-8 mm long, with an awn 1.0-1.5 cm long. A tall-grass prairie plant that usually grows in association with *Andropogon scoparius*. Indiangrass is occasional in our area in sandy openings of oak woodlands.

53. SORGHUM

A genus of about 20 species, all but one native to the Old World. The annuals *S. vulgare* Pers. and *S. sudanense* (Piper) Stapf are widely cultivated in this country, the former for grain and the latter for forage.

*1. **SORGHUM HALEPENSE** (L.) Pers. JOHNSONGRASS (Fig. 156). Tall coarse perennial, with stout creeping rhizomes, stout culms, broad blades and large open panicles. With the possible exception of bermuda grass, *Cynodon dactylon,* this is the most widespread and frequent grass in Texas. Johnsongrass thrives in disturbed soils, especially those receiving a good moisture supply. It grows throughout the Coastal Bend area. Although widely used for forage, Johnsongrass is responsible for prussic-acid poisoning in grazing animals under certain conditions of growth.

Fig. 154. *Setaria texana*. Inflorescence.

Fig. 155. *Sorghastrum nutans*. Plant and spikelet with pedicel of totally reduced paired spikelet.

Fig. 156. *Sorghum halepense*. Inflorescence and spikelet pair.

54. SPARTINA Cordgrass

Stout, often tall perennials, usually with thick, creeping rhizomes and long tough blades. Spikelets one-flowered, usually closely placed on one side of short spicate inflorescence branches. A genus of about 16 species, these mostly along the coast of the Americas, Europe and Africa Mobberly, 1956). Our plants are native warm-season perennials.

KEY TO THE SPECIES

Culms usually in large dense clumps; rhizomes lacking; panicle with 10-50 short appressed spikelet-bearing branches, these obscuring the inflorescence axis; spikelets mostly 6-8 mm long
S. spartinae

Culms usually single or in small clusters from an extensive system of creeping rhizomes; panicle with 2-15 spikelet-bearing branches, these usually not appressed nor obscuring the inflorescence axis; spikelets 8-12 mm long

Culms mostly 1-2 meters or more tall, soft and spongy at the base, arising from thick, flaccid, whitish rhizomes; spikelets mostly 9-11 mm long; leaf blades mostly 5-15 mm wide
S. alterniflora

Culms usually less than 1 meter tall, slender and firm, arising from slender, wiry rhizomes; spikelets mostly 6-8 mm long; leaf blades rarely over 3 mm broad   *S. patens*

1. SPARTINA ALTERNIFLORA Loisel. SMOOTH CORDGRASS (Fig. 157). Culms to 2.5 meters tall. Inflorescence branches 3-25, 5-15 cm long, loosely appressed to the main axis. Occasional to locally abundant in swales and bays along the coast. Of little grazing value, due to the tough, coarse herbage. Our plants commonly referred to *S. alterniflora* var. *glabra* (Michx.) Fern. but Mobberly (1956) does not recognize this segregate.

*2. SPARTINA PATENS (Ait.) Muhl. MARSHHAY CORDGRASS (Fig. 158). Culms to as much as 1.5 meters tall but usually less than 1 meter tall. Panicles 3-15 cm long, bearing 2-15 branches 2-7 cm long.

Rather frequent along salt water swamps, bays and tidal rivers. Of fair to poor grazing value. Our plants are referrable to *S. patens* var. *juncea* Hitchc., a variety not recognized by Mobberly (1956).

*3. SPARTINA SPARTINAE (Trin.) Hitchc. GULF CORDGRASS (Fig. 159). Culms mostly 80-150 mm tall but occasionally taller. Leaf blades long, firm, narrow (5 mm or less broad) and involute. Spikelets mostly 6-8 mm long.

Frequent and locally abundant in moist saline sites throughout our area, mostly on clayey soils. Many pastures immediately bordering the Gulf and the coastal bays are comprised of dense, almost pure stands of this grass. It rates only fair as a forage grass.

55. SPHENOPHOLIS Wedgescale

Slender short-lived perennials or annuals with weak culms, flat blades and narrow panicles. Spikelets 2-3 flowered, disarticulating below the glumes. Species 6, distributed in North America and the West Indies.

1. SPHENOPHOLIS OBTUSATA (Michx.) Scribn. PRAIRIE WEDGESCALE (Fig. 160). Widely distributed throughout the United States, this cool-season annual or weak perennial is infrequent in our area. It generally grows in moist sandy or sandy loam, in partial shade.

Fig. 157. *Spartina alterniflora.* Inflorescence and spikelet.

Fig. 158. *Spartina patens*. Inflorescence.
Fig. 159 a-b. *Spartina spartinae*. Inflorescence and spikelet.

Fig. 160. *Sphenopholis obtusata*. Plant and spikelet.

56. SPOROBOLUS Dropseed

Annuals and perennials with open or contracted panicles and one-flowered spikelets. Spikelets similar in general aspect to those of *Muhlenbergia* but lemmas thin, one-nerved and awnless.

Species about 100, distributed in the temperate and subtropical regions of the world. The 9 species of our area are warm-season plants that flower from late spring to autumn.

Fig. 161. *Sporobolus airoides*. Plant and spikelet with glumes separated from the floret.

KEY TO THE SPECIES

Flowering culms from stout, widely spreading rhizomes; panicle contracted, spikelike; plants of saline soils, mostly on the seashore *S. virginicus*
Flowering culms from non-rhizomatous base
  Spikelets 3-7 mm long
    Second glume 2/3 to 3/4 as long as the lemma
      Spikelets 5-7 mm long; lemmas pubescent *S. asper* var. *canovirens*
      Spikelets 3-5 mm long; lemmas glabrous *S. asper* var. *hookeri*
    Second glume about as long as the lemma; spikelets about 3 mm long; lemmas glabrous
      Inflorescence branches in distinct whorls, usually less than 4 cm long
        Panicle dense, contracted, the branches 1-2 cm long, appressed or ascending *S. purpurascens*
        Panicle more or less open, the branches 2-3 cm long, at maturity rather widely spreading *S. junceus*
      Inflorescence branches not in distinct whorls, usually more than 4 cm long *S. tharpii*
  Spikelets 2.2 mm or less long
    Lower panicle branches mostly in whorls of 3-8, the longer branches bare of spikelets near the base *S. pyramidatus*
    Lower panicle branches single at each node
      Glumes subequal, broad and often irregularly toothed; panicle spikelike, the erect-appressed branchlets spikelet-bearing to the base *S. poiretii*
      Glumes acute, the first about half as long as the second; panicle spikelike or open; the lower branches bare of spikelets near the base
        Collar of leaf sheath with lateral tufts of hair (occasionally glabrate in age); culms few to several in a cluster, never in large dense clumps *S. cryptandrus*
        Collar of leaf sheath glabrous; culms usually in large dense clumps *S. airoides*

*1. SPOROBOLUS A I R O I D E S (Torr.) Torr. ALKALI SACATON (Fig. 161). Coarse perennial with culms mostly 60-120 cm tall, usually in dense clumps. Blades mostly 4 mm or less broad, long and tapering to a fine point, involute on drying. Inflorescence large, many-flowered. Alkali sacaton is infrequent in the Coastal Bend area, growing in swales and marshy borders of streams, often in saline areas. All plants of the Texas coastal area have densely-flowered panicles with relatively short, stiffly erect-spreading branches and appressed branchlets and spikelets. These appear closer in general aspect to *S. airoides* var. *wrightii* (Munro ex Scribn.) Gould (*S. wrightii* Munro ex Scribn.) than to the typical variety.

*2. SPOROBOLUS ASPER (Michx.) Kunth var. *canovirens* (Nash) Shinners (*Sporobolus clandestinus* (Bieler) Hitchc. in part). (Fig. 162). Panicle 5-10 cm long, narrow, with erect-appressed branches. A rather tall bunchgrass with stiffly erect culms in small clusters. Occasional in our area, mostly in open, sandy-loam sites.

*2a. SPOROBOLUS ASPER (Michx.) Kunth var. *hookeri* (Trin.) Vasey. MEADOW DROPSEED. Culms slender, stiffly erect, in small clumps. Panicle contracted, small, usually developed on branches at the upper nodes as well as terminally. Occasional on open pastureland in heavy clay.

*3. SPOROBOLUS C R Y P T A N D R U S (Torr.) Gray. SAND DROPSEED (Fig. 163). Inflorescence usually partially or mostly enclosed in the sheath. Sand dropseed is present on disturbed sites throughout the state, especially on sandy or sandy loam sites. It is occasional but never abundant on well-managed native pastures. This somewhat "weedy" perennial is rated only fair as a forage plant in our area.

4. SPOROBOLUS JUNCEUS (Michx.) Kunth. PINEYWOODS DROPSEED. A tufted perennial, frequent in the pine barrens of the eastern Coastal Plain and extending southwestward to Texas. Reported by Jones *et al.* (1961) in our area.

*5. SPOROBOLUS POIRETII (Roem. & Schult.) Hitchc. RATTAIL SMUTGRASS (Fig. 164). A rather coarse, tufted perennial that is widespread throughout the American tropics and subtropics. Hitchcock (1950) stated that this apparently is introduced in America. In the Coastal Bend, rattail smutgrass is occasional in sandy loam soils, usually in yards or other disturbed places. It is of poor grazing value.

Fig. 162. *Sporobolus asper* var. *canovirens*. Inflorescence and spikelet.

Fig. 163. *Sporobolus cryptandrus.* Plant and spikelet with glumes separated from the floret.

Fig. 164 a-b. *Sporobolus poiretii*. Inflorescence and spikelet.
Fig. 165 a-b. *Sporobolus pyramidatus*. Inflorescence and spikelet.

*6. SPOROBOLUS PURPURASCENS (Swartz) Hamilt. PURPLE DROPSEED. Moderately tall, tufted perennial, generally similar to *S. junceus* but with a distribution of South Texas to the West Indies and Brazil. Occasional in the coastal prairie, in loose sandy soil.

*7. SPOROBOLUS PYRAMIDATUS (Lam.) Hitchc. WHORLED DROPSEED (Fig. 165). Low tufted perennial. Blades thin, flat, glabrous or with a few long hairs near the base. Ligule a fringed membrane 0.5 mm or less long. Spikelets 1.6-2.0 mm long. Inflorescence mostly 4-7 cm long, with short, spreading branches, at least some in definite whorls. Occasional to frequent on fine textured soils, usually in saline areas or sites with poor physical soil structure. Of poor grazing value.

8. SPOROBOLUS THARPII Hitchc.

PADRE ISLAND DROPSEED (Fig. 166). Rather coarse perennial with culms in dense clumps. Panicle 15-30 cm long, with stiffly erect-spreading branches as much as 15 cm long. This species is occasional in our area on sand and calcarious shell soils along the ocean and coastal bays. It apparently is endemic to Texas.

Fig. 166. *Sporobolus tharpii*. Inflorescence and spikelet.

Fig. 167. *Sporobolus virginicus*. Plant and spikelet.

*9. SPOROBOLUS VIRGINICUS (L.) Kunth. SEASHORE DROPSEED (Fig. 167). Low coarse perennial with creeping rhizomes, firm closely crowded leaves with conspicuously overlapping sheaths and short blades, and short, contracted panicles. Locally frequent in sandy soils along salt water, usually forming dense stands similar to bermudagrass. Of poor to fair grazing value.

57. STENOTAPHRUM

Stoloniferous perennials with succulent herbage, broad flat leaf blades, and inflorescences of stout flattened spikes with the spikelets more or less embedded in the thickened axis. Species about five, mostly on islands of the Pacific but one in the American tropics and subtropics.

*1. STENOTAPHRUM SECUNDATUM (Walt.) Kuntze. ST. AUGUSTINE GRASS (Fig. 168). This low, mat-forming, coarse-bladed perennial is commonly used as a lawngrass in southern and southeastern Texas. Although lacking rhizomes, it successfully competes against bermudagrass when supplied with adequate moisture and fertility. St. Augustine grass grows only as an escape and usually is found in the vicinity of maintained lawns. It seldom produces seed and is propogated by sprigs and sod-clumps.

58. STIPA

Tufted perennials with single-flowered spikelets in open or contracted panicles. Glumes large, thin, persistent. Lemma firm, awned at the apex and with a sharp-pointed callus at the base.

A large genus, best represented on the plains and prairies of the temperate regions of the world. All but 2 of the 11 Texas species are present in the western and north-central portions of the state.

*1. STIPA LEUCOTRICHA Trin. and Rupr. TEXAS WINTERGRASS (Fig. 169). Cool-season bunchgrass, flowering from early spring till summer. Although this grass is of considerable value for early spring green forage, the sharp-pointed, long-awned fruits are objectionable when mature. Texas wintergrass grows on all soil types, but in our area is most abundant on the clay loams. It is our most common perennial cool-season grass.

59. TRACHYPOGON

Moderately large bunchgrass, with flowering culms bearing a single spicate raceme (paired in some Mexican species). Species about 9, distributed from southern United States to Central and South America.

*1. TRACHYPOGON SECUNDUS (Presl) Scribn. CRINKLEAWN (Fig. 170). Warm-season perennial bunchgrass. Culms, 50-120 cm tall, hispid at the nodes. Occasional on open pastures, more frequent south and west of our area. *Trachypogon montufari* (H.B.K.) Nees in Ed I. of Hitchcock's Manual.

60. TRAGUS Burgrass

A small genus of tropical-subtropical grasses, with 2 species in southern and southeastern U. S., both probably introduced.

1. TRAGUS RACEMOSA (L.) All. STALKED BURGRASS. Annual with geniculate - spreading culms 5-30 cm tall. Ligule a dense ring of short hairs. Blades short, flat, 2-5 mm broad, usually with coarsely hispid-ciliate margins. Inflorescence a spike-like panicle mostly 2-8 cm long, with spikelets in short-pedicelled bur-like clusters. Reported by Jones *et al.* (1961) to have been collected by Heller at Corpus Christi.

61. TRICHLORIS

Spikelets 2-5-flowered; lemmas 3-nerved the nerves extending into awns. A genus of three warm-season perennial bunchgrasses, distributed in southern United States, Mexico and Argentina.

*1. TRICHLORIS PLURIFLORA Fourn. FOURFLOWERED TRICHLORIS (Fig. 171). Culms 50-120 cm tall. Leaf blades 5-10 mm broad. Inflorescence branches 7-16 cm long, mostly in one or two irregular verticels at the culm apex. Spikelets with 3-5 florets, the upper rudimentary. Lateral awns of the lemmas short or absent. A moderately large bunchgrass of excellent forage value. Occasional on many sites.

62. TRICHONEURA

A group of about 9 species, these mainly in Africa and South America, with one species in the United States.

*1. TRICHONEURA ELEGANS Swallen. SILVEUSGRASS (Fig. 172). Rather robust annual with erect or partially decumbent many-noded culms. Inflorescence a panicle with spikelets short-pedicelled on the main branches. Spikelets mostly 5- to 8-flowered, with long, 1-nerved, acuminate glumes and 3-nerved awnless or mucronate lemmas. Margins of lemmas conspicuously ciliate on the lower half.

An interesting native warm-season annual of local distribution, known only from southern and south-central Texas and Tamaulipas, Mexico. Collected in deep sands on Padre Island and at two locations in San Patricio County.

Fig. 168. *Stenotaphrum secundatum*. Plant and spikelet.

Fig. 169. *Stipa leucotricha*. Inflorescence and spikelet.

Fig. 170. *Trachypogon secundus*. Plant and spikelet.

Fig. 171. *Trichloris pluriflora*. Inflorescence and spikelet.

Fig. 172. *Trichoneura elegans*. Inflorescence and spikelet.

63. TRIDENS

Perennials with several-flowered spikelets in open or contracted panicles. Glumes large, 1- to 3-nerved, awnless. Lemmas 3-nerved, awnless, or the midnerve extended as a short mucro. A small North American genus, recently reduced in size by the exclusion of several species listed in Hitchcock's Manual (1950) which are now grouped in the genus *Erioneuron* (Tateoka, 1961). Our species are all native warm-season bunchgrasses.

KEY TO THE SPECIES

Inflorescence an open panicle, the spikelets on the middle of the upper portions of long slender branches
    Lemmas 1.8-2.5 mm long; spikelets mostly 4-6 mm long; leaf blades rarely over 4 mm broad
        T. eragrostoides
    Lemmas mostly 3.5-5 mm long; spikelets usually more than 6 mm long
        Panicles mostly 8-15 cm long, the lower branches rarely over 6 cm long; leaf blades 1-4 mm broad; spikelets usually light yellowish green tinged with pink or purple   *T. texanus*
        Panicles mostly 15-30 cm long, the lower branches to 15 cm or more long; leaf blades 4-10 mm broad; spikelets usually dark purple at maturity   *T. flavus*
Inflorescence a contracted, slender spikelike panicle, the branches short, appressed, spikelet-bearing to near the base
    Glumes equalling or exceeding the uppermost floret; panicle large and dense   *T. strictus*
    Glumes not or only slightly exceeding the first lemma
        Lateral nerves of the lemma glabrous, the lemma entirely glabrous or with a few hairs at the extreme base; lemmas with or without mucronate tip, the mucro when present less than 0.5 mm long   *T. albescens*
        Lateral nerves of the lemma hairy, at least below
            Panicle densely-flowered, usually more than 1 cm broad; lemmas mucronate, the mucro often over 5 mm long   *T. congestus*
            Panicle not densely flowered, usually less than 1 cm broad; lemmas lacking a mucro or with a mucro much less than 5 cm long   *T. muticus*

*1. TRIDENS ALBESCENS (Vasey) Woot. & Standl. WHITE TRIDENS (Fig. 173). Inflorescence whitish or violet tinged. Herbage and spikelets glabrous. White tridens is occasional to frequent on fine-textured soils, usually growing in moist or poorly drained areas. It is especially frequent in roadside ditches. Of fair grazing value, this grass contributes significantly to the forage in many pastures.

*2. TRIDENS CONGESTUS (L. H. Dewey) Nash. PINK TRIDENS (Fig. 174). Culms in small clumps. Herbage glabrous or essentially so. Ligule a dense fringe of hairs mostly 0.5 mm or less long. Leaf long, flat, narrow, bright green beneath, glaucous above. Inflorescence contracted, congested, mostly 5-10 cm long. Spikelets light colored, rosy or light violet tinged. Lemmas with tufts of short hair on all 3 nerves from the middle to near the base (but not at the base).

Pink tridens is occasional in scattered stands throughout our area. It is generally adapted to poorly drained tight soils, and occurs both on upland clay sites and in the saline marshy grasslands bordering the Gulf.

*3. TRIDENS ERAGROSTOIDES (Vasey & Scribn.) Nash. LOVEGRASS TRIDENS (Fig. 175). Panicle open, 10-30 cm long, with slender drooping branches. Spikelets small, dark purple at maturity. Occasional on clays and clay loams, usually along fence rows or in the protection of shrubs. Of excellent forage value.

*4. TRIDENS FLAVUS (I.) Hitchc. PURPLETOP (Fig. 176). Culms slender, mostly 1-1.5 meters tall, the large open panicles with gracefully drooping branches. Frequent in and along woodlands through eastern and East-Central United States, purpletop is a common grass of eastern Texas but is infrequent in our area. It grows mainly on sandy soils in woodland sites.

Fig. 173. *Tridens albescens*. Plant, spikelet, and floret.

Fig. 174. *Tridens congestus*. Inflorescence and spikelet.

Fig. 175. *Tridens eragrostoides*. Inflorescence and spikelet.

Fig. 176. *Tridens flavus*. Inflorescence and spikelet.

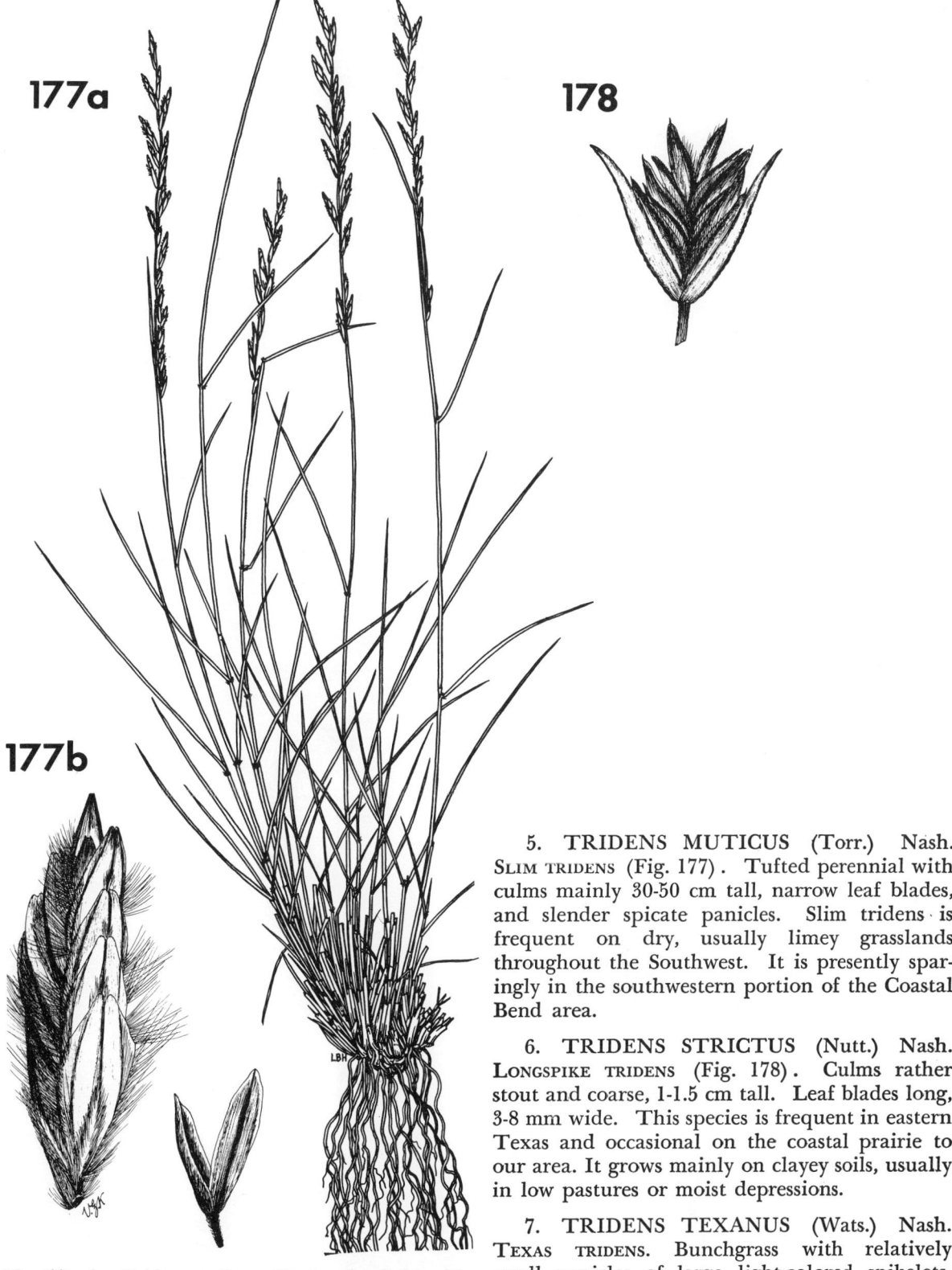

5. **TRIDENS MUTICUS** (Torr.) Nash. SLIM TRIDENS (Fig. 177). Tufted perennial with culms mainly 30-50 cm tall, narrow leaf blades, and slender spicate panicles. Slim tridens is frequent on dry, usually limey grasslands throughout the Southwest. It is presently sparingly in the southwestern portion of the Coastal Bend area.

6. **TRIDENS STRICTUS** (Nutt.) Nash. LONGSPIKE TRIDENS (Fig. 178). Culms rather stout and coarse, 1-1.5 cm tall. Leaf blades long, 3-8 mm wide. This species is frequent in eastern Texas and occasional on the coastal prairie to our area. It grows mainly on clayey soils, usually in low pastures or moist depressions.

7. **TRIDENS TEXANUS** (Wats.) Nash. TEXAS TRIDENS. Bunchgrass with relatively small panicles of large light-colored spikelets. Lemmas thin and somewhat papery. Occasional on sand loam or clay loam soils in our area.

Fig. 177 a-b. *Tridens muticus*. Plant and spikelet with glumes separated from the florets.

Fig. 178. *Tridens strictus*. Spikelet.

Fig. 179. *Triplasis purpurea*. Inflorescence and spikelet.

64. TRIPLASIS

A genus of two species, one annual and one perennial, distributed in central and eastern United States.

1. TRIPLASIS PURPUREA (Walt.) Chapm. PURPLE SANDGRASS (Fig. 179). Tufted warm-season annual. Culms 30-100 cm tall, with numerous, pubescent nodes. Inflorescence relatively small and few-flowered. Spikelets with 2-4 florets. Lemmas 3-4 mm long, with densely short-pubescent nerves. Occasional in sandy woods openings. Of no forage singificance.

65. TRIPSACUM

Large coarse perennials, with broad flat blades. Spikelets unisexual, borne in a terminal spike or two to several spicate branches. Pistillate spikelets hard and bony, borne below the 2-flowered staminate spikelets. A genus of 7 species, entirely American in distribution and mostly in the tropics and subtropics.

1. TRIPSACUM DACTYLOIDES (L.) L. EASTERN GAMAGRASS (Fig. 180). Culms mostly 1.5-3 meters tall, in large clumps from a hard knotty base. Blades long and flat, broad or rather narrow. Eastern gamagrass is most frequent in our area along banks of brackish streams and ditches near the Gulf.

66. TRISETUM

Spikelets 2—to several-flowered. Glumes about equalling the florets. Lemma toothed at the apex, bearing a geniculate, twisted awn between the teeth. A genus of about 50 species, distributed in the temperate and arctic regions of both hemispheres.

*1. TRISETUM INTERRUPTUM Buckl. PRAIRIE TRISETUM (Fig. 181). Tufted cool-season annual with a contracted narrow panicle. Spikelets about 5 mm long, 2-flowered. Infrequent in our area, growing on disturbed sandy soil.

67. TRITICUM

Annuals with flat blades and a stout terminal spike, with spikelets solitary at the nodes. A genus of about 10 species, native to Europe and western Asia.

*1. TRITICUM AESTIVUM L. WHEAT (Fig. 182). Culms mostly 60-100 cm tall, freely branching at the base. Spikelets broad, several-flowered, long-awned to awnless. Occasional as a cool-season annual, mainly along road right of ways from chance seedings.

Fig 180. *Tripsacum dactyloides*. Inflorescence.

Fig. 181. *Trisetum interruptum*. Inflorescence and spikelet.

Fig. 182. *Triticum aestivum*. Inflorescence.

68. UNIOLA

Moderately large perennial grasses with open paniculate inflorescence. Spikelets 3- to many-flowered, usually with reduced florets below as well as above the fertile ones. A genus of about 9 species, all American, 6 in the United States.

KEY TO THE SPECIES

Blades firm, involute, less than 1 cm broad; plant of coastal dunes, with long rhizomes
U. paniculata

Blades relatively thin, flat, at least some 1-2 cm broad; woodland plants, with rhizomes not over a few centimeters long when present
U. latifolia

*1. UNIOLA LATIFOLIA Michx. BROADLEAF UNIOLA (Fig. 183). Culms in small clumps, mostly 80-150 cm tall. Inflorescence an open, drooping panicle, with large flat spikelets borne on slender branches. Spikelets mostly 8- to 12-flowered. Occasional in moist sandy woods, most frequently on streambanks. This grass develops little herbage and is not an important forage plant.

2. UNIOLA PANICULATA L. SEA OATS (Fig. 184). Culms 1-1.5 meters tall, from creeping rhizomes. Spikelets as in *U. latifolia* but bearing 10 to 20 or more florets. Frequent on sandy dunes along the sea shore and on the coastal islands. Of fair forage value.

69. VASEYOCHLOA

A monotypic genus, with the single species known only from southern Texas.

*1. VASEYOCHLOA MULTINERVOSA (Vasey) Hitchc. TEXASGRASS (Fig. 185). Tufted warm-season perennial. Culms in small clumps, slender, mostly 50-100 cm tall, bearing drooping panicles of rather large, several-flowered spikelets. Lemmas 7-11-nerved, awnless, slightly hairy on the lower portion of the back. Caryopsis dark brown or black at maturity.

An interesting endemic with no apparent close relatives. Reported as "rare" in Hitchcock's Manual (1950), this species is locally abundant on sandy sites in San Patricio and Kleberg counties. It also is reported from Padre Island, Nueces County, and probably is occasional on sands throughout the central and southern portion of the Coastal Bend area.

70. VULPIA

A genus of mostly annual grasses, these distributed for the most part in temperate Europe and North and South America. Although the genus *Vulpia* has been widely recognized throughout the world, most American botanists have followed Hitchcock (1950) in including these grasses in the genus *Festuca*.

*1. VULPIA OCTOFLORA (Walt.) Rydb. (*Festuca octoflora* Walt.) SIXWEEKS FESCUE (Fig. 186). Tufted cool-season annual with involute blades 1-2 mm broad. Inflorescence a contracted panicle or raceme usually 4-15 cm long. Spikelets mostly 6-11-flowered with narrow pointed glumes and glabrous or scabrous awn-tipped lemmas, the awn usually 3-6 mm long. Commonly known as "sixweeks fescue" this grass is widely distributed and native throughout Texas and many other parts of the United States. It is highly variable in size and pubescence characters and several varieties have been recognized. Present on most all sites in the Coastal Bend region during the cooler months, this weedy grass is most frequent around ant beds and other locally disturbed soil areas.

71. WILLKOMMIA

A genus of 4 species, 3 in South Africa and one in Texas and Argentina.

*1. WILLKOMMIA TEXANA Hitchc. TEXAS WILLKOMMIA (Fig. 187). Spikelets 1-flowered, sessile on short branches scattered along the main culm axis. Spikelet about 4 mm long, the second glume and lemma about equal, the first glume shorter.

A low, tufted warm-season perennial, occasional in hard tight soil bordering cattle tanks, swales, and small lakes. This interesting endemic is easily overlooked and probably is much more common than the record indicates. It has no significance as a forage plant.

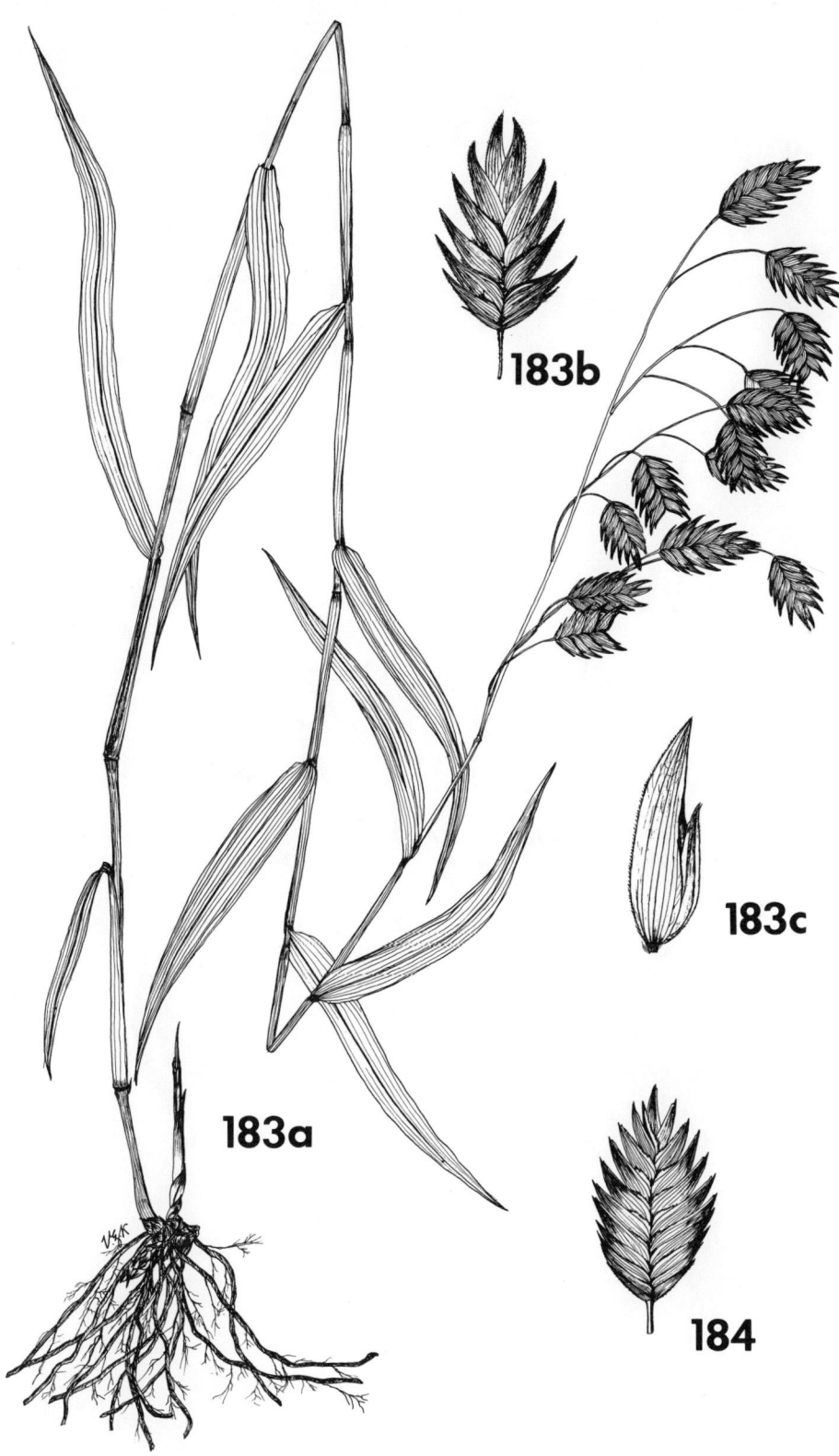

Fig. 183 a-c. *Uniola latifolia*. Plant, spikelet and floret.
Fig. 184. *Uniola paniculata*. Spikelet.

Fig. 185. *Vaseyochloa multinervosa*. Plant, spikelet, floret and caryopsis.

Fig. 186. *Vulpia octoflora*. Plant and spikelet.
Fig. 187 a-b. *Willkommia texana*. Plant and spikelet.

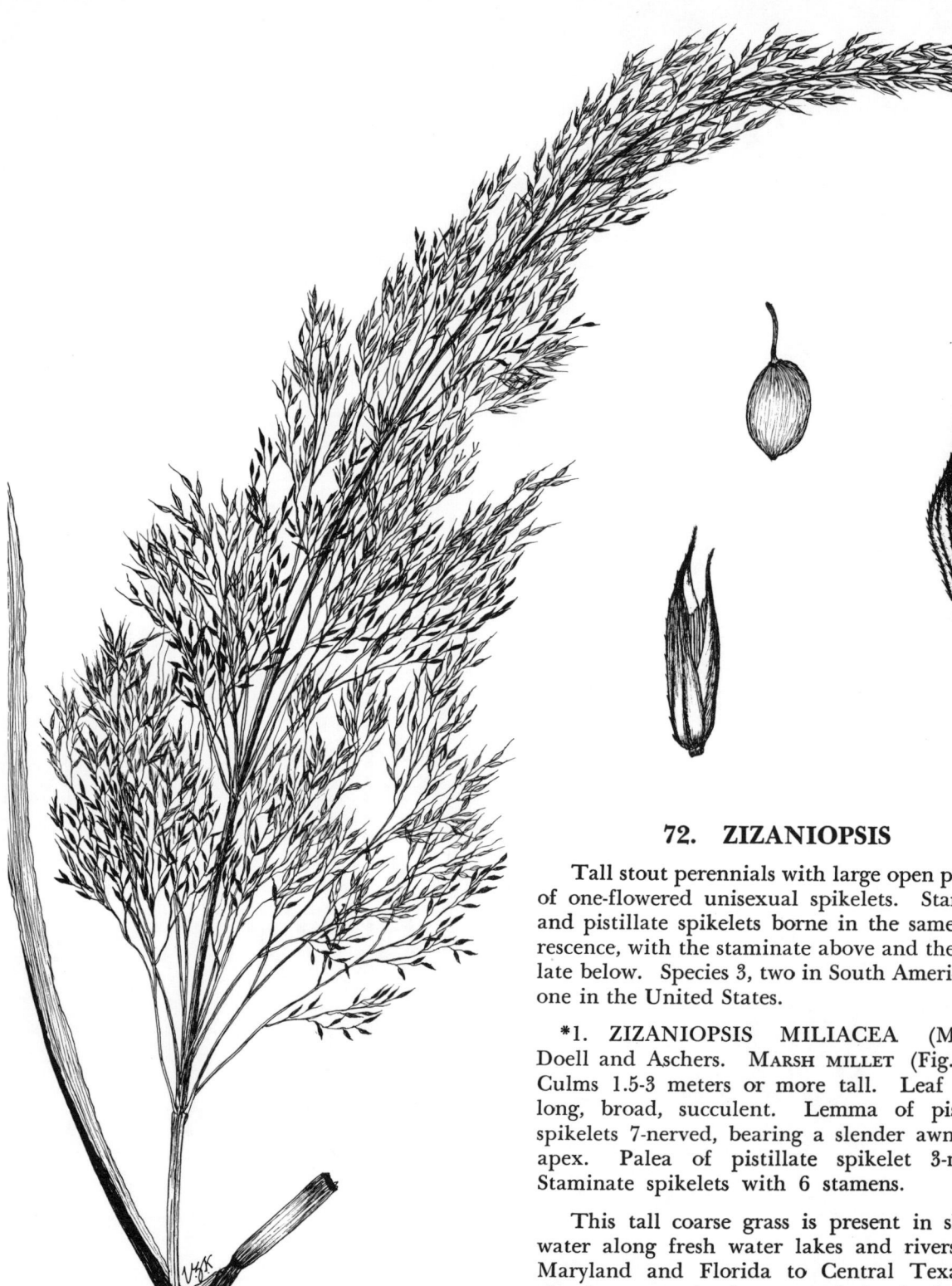

Fig. 188. *Zizaniopsis miliacea.* Inflorescence, staminate spikelet, pistillate spikelet, and caryopsis.

72. ZIZANIOPSIS

Tall stout perennials with large open panicles of one-flowered unisexual spikelets. Staminate and pistillate spikelets borne in the same inflorescence, with the staminate above and the pistillate below. Species 3, two in South America and one in the United States.

*1. ZIZANIOPSIS MILIACEA (Michx.) Doell and Aschers. MARSH MILLET (Fig. 188). Culms 1.5-3 meters or more tall. Leaf blades long, broad, succulent. Lemma of pistillate spikelets 7-nerved, bearing a slender awn at its apex. Palea of pistillate spikelet 3-nerved. Staminate spikelets with 6 stamens.

This tall coarse grass is present in shallow water along fresh water lakes and rivers from Maryland and Florida to Central Texas. It also is present in dense stands in the brackish coastal marshes. Although of value for wildlife food and cover, marsh millet tends to clog up water ways and lake shores. It is frequent in our area, especially in Calhoun and Aransas counties.

GLOSSARY*

Acuminate: gradually tapering to a point or acumen.

Acute: pointed, not abruptly nor long-extended but making an angle of less than 90 degrees.

Adventive: a term used to denote an exotic species that has become established from chance or accidental seeding.

Annual: with a life span of one year or less.

Antrorse: pointed upward or toward the apex. The opposite of *retrorse*.

Apiculate: with a short, sharp point.

Articulation: joint.

Auricle: literally "ear"; applied to the lateral lobes or projections of tissue present at the apex of the leaf sheath in some grasses.

Awn: bristle or stiff hair at the end of an organ such as the lemma or glume.

Bearded: in reference to culm nodes; hairy.

Bract: a reduced leaf structure, often scale-like; the glumes, lemma, and palea are referred to as bracts.

Bracteate: provided with a bract or bracts.

Bristle: stiff hair or awn; in *Setaria*, *Pennisetum* and a few other grasses, the inflorescence branches immediately below the spikelets are reduced to bristles.

Capitate: head-like.

Capitallate: bearing a minute globular swelling at the apex.

Caryopsis: the one-seeded grain or fruit of grasses.

Ciliate: fringed with hairs on the margin, like eyelashes.

Cleistogene: plant bearing *cleistogamous* flowers (flowers that are self-fertilized and remain unopened).

Concavo-convex: "hollowed out" on one side and "bulged out" on the other.

Cordate: heart-shaped, applied to grass blades that are short, broad, and appear notched at the end of attachment.

Culm: stem of the grass plant.

Deciduous: falling regularly or in season from a definite joint or callus.

Decumbent: applied to stems that curve upward from a reclining or horizontal base.

Digitate: radiating from a common point or base, as the fingers (digits) of the hand; common bermudagrass, *Cynodon dactylon*, has an inflorescence of digitately arranged spicate branches.

Dioecious: flowers imperfect and the male and female flowers borne on separate plants.

Dorsal: the back side or surface; the surface of a structure away from the central stalk or axis.

Fertile lemma: the lemma of the floret bearing the ovary or caryopsis (term used in reference to spikelets of the tribes *Paniceae* and *Andropogoneae*).

Floret: the unit of the spikelet consisting usually of lemma, palea, and the flower (lodicules, stamens, pistil).

Geniculate: abruptly bent, as at the elbow or knee joint.

Glabrous: smooth, without hairs.

Glumes: the pair of sterile bracts usually present at the base of the spikelet.

Hirsute: hairy with long, rather distinct hairs.

Hispid: hairy with stiff hairs.

Imperfect: with unisexual flowers or florets (also applied to spikelets); bearing either male or female reproductive structures but not both in the same flower.

Indurate: hard.

Inflorescence: the flowering portion of the plant.

Lacerate: torn or irregularly cleft.

Lemma: the lowermost of the two bracts of a grass floret.

Ligule: a membranous or hairy appendage on the inner (adaxial) surface of the grass leaf at the junction of sheath and blade.

Monoecious: flowers unisexual (imperfect) and with male and female flowers borne on the same plant.

---
*Definitions for the most part taken from "Grasses of Southwestern United States" (Gould, 1951).

Mucro: see mucronate.

Mucronate: abruptly tipped with a short, straight point or mucro, like the mere projection of the midnerve.

Neuter: without male or female reproductive structures.

Oblong: two or three times longer than broad, with abruptly rounded ends and with nearly parallel sides.

Obpyriform: pear shaped, with the point of attachment at the large end. The opposite of *pyriform*.

Obtuse: blunt or rounded (apex or base), usually making an angle of more than 90 degrees.

Orbicular: disc-shaped, circular in outline.

Oval: similar to *oblong*, with rounded but not abruptly rounded ends.

Ovate: opposite of obovate; egg-shaped, with the broader end nearer the base.

Ovoid: an egg-shaped solid.

Palea: the uppermost of the two scale-like bracts at the base of the flower in the grass floret.

Panicle: a compound inflorescence, with at least some of the branches rebranched.

Pappila: a nipple-shaped projection.

Pedicel: the stalk of a single flower; in grasses applied to the support of a single spikelet.

Peduncle: a flower stalk, usually applied to the support of several flowers or spikelets.

Perennial: with a life span of more than one year.

Perfect floret: floret with both male and female reproductive structures.

Pilose: soft-hairy, the hairs relatively long.

Plumose: feather-like, having fine hairs on either side.

Primary inflorescence branch: branch arising directly from the main inflorescence axis.

Puberulent: clothed with very fine hairs or down.

Pubescent: the hairiness of plants.

Pulvinus: a gland-like swelling in the axil of a leaf or branch.

Pustulate: blister-like.

Raceme: an inflorescence with one-flowered pedicels (or pedicels bearing a single spikelet) arising directly from the main axis; a simply branched inflorescence.

Rachilla: the axis of a spikelet upon which the floret or florets are inserted.

Rachis: the axis of a spike or spicate raceme; the axis of a pinnately compound leaf.

Retrorse: pointed downward or toward the base; the opposite of antrorse.

Rhizome: an underground stem; recognized by the regular nodes and internodes.

Rudiment: the rudiment of a spikelet is formed by structures of a reduced sterile floret.

Rugose: rough, with minute knobs or projections.

Scabrous: roughened with stout projections.

Sessile: without a stalk or pedicel.

Spathe: an enlarged, sheathing bract as that which surrounds the spadix inflorescence of the call a lily *(Zantedeschia)*, and the jack-in-the pulpit *(Arisaema)*.

Spicate: spikelike.

Spike: an unbranched inflorescence in which the flowers (or spikelets) are sessile on the rachis.

Sterile lemma: lemma of rudimentary or staminate lower floret of the panicoid spikelet.

Stolon: a specialized trailing or decumbent stem functioning to spread or, when broken off, to reproduce the plant.

Style: the usually slender portions of the pistil that bear the stigmas or stigmatic surfaces. Grass fruits, with the exception of some bamboos, have two styles.

Terete: circular in cross section.

Truncate: as though abruptly "chopped off" at the base or apex.

Tuberculate: bearing knob-like projections.

Villous: densely hairy with long, soft hairs.

Verticel: the arrangement of organs or appendages (as branches, leaves, or flowers) in a circle around an axis.

Vestigial: almost totally reduced, with just a vestige remaining.

LITERATURE CITED

Avdulov, N. P. 1931. Karyo-systematische Untersuchugen der Familie Gramineen. Bull. Appl. Bot. suppl. 44. (Russian with German summary).

Banks, D. J. 1963. Taxonomy of *Paspalum*, group *Setacea*. Unpub. Ph.D. dissertation, Univ. of Georgia, Athens.

Beetle, A. A. 1955. The four subfamilies of the Gramineae. Bull. Torrey Bot. Club 82:196-197.

Bloodgood, D. W., R. E. Patterson and R. L. Smith. 1954. Water evaporation studies in Texas. Tex. Agr. Expt. Sta. Bull. 787. 83 pp.

Box, Thadis W. 1957. Vegetational analyses and the determination of range condition classes on selected areas of the Welder Wildlife Refuge. Unpublished M.S. Thesis. Texas A&M University. 98 pp.

Brown, W. V. 1958. Leaf anatomy in grass systematics. Bot. Gaz. 119:170-178.

DeLisle, Donald G. 1963. Taxonomy and distribution of the genus *Cenchrus*. Iowa State Jour. Sci. 37(3):259-351.

Duval, Jouve, J. 1875. Histotaxic des feuilles de Graminees. Ann. Sci. Nat. Bot. ser. 6, 1:294-371.

Ebinger, J. E. 1962. Validity of the grass species *Digitaria adscendens*. Brittona 14:248-253.

Emery, W. H. P. 1958. A cyto-taxonomic study of *Setaria macrostachya* (Gramineae) and its relatives in the southwestern United States and Mexico. Bull. Torr. Bot. Club 84(2):94-105.

Gould, F. W. 1951. Grasses of southwestern United States. Univ. of Ariz. Biol. Sci. Bull. No. 7. Univ. of Arizona Press, Tucson.

―――――. 1955. *Parapholis incurva* and *Chloris polydactyla* in Texas. Field & Lab. 23(3-4):83.

―――――. 1957. Texas grasses—a preliminary checklist. Tex. Agr. Expt. Sta. MP-240. 33 pp. mimeo.

―――――. 1962. Texas plants, a checklist and ecological summary. Tex. Agr. Expt. Sta. Misc. Publ. MP-585. 112 pp. 11 illust. (released to public Jan. 1963).

―――――. 1963. Cytotaxonomy of *Digitaria sanguinalis* and *D. adscendens*. Brittonia 15:241-244.

――――― and T. W. Box. 1959. Grasses of the Texas Coastal Bend. Welder Wildlife Found. Cont. 34. Series C. 85 pp. mimeo.

Henrard, J. T. 1950. Monograph of the genus *Digitaria*. XII + 999 pp. Leyden, Universitare Pers Leiden.

Hitchcock, A. S. 1926. *Eragrostis hypnoides* and *Eragrostis reptans*. Rhodora, 28:113-115.

―――――. 1950. Manual of the grasses of the United States. U.S.D.A. Misc. Pub. 200. 1051 pp. Revised ed.

Jones, F. B., C. M. Rowell, and M. C. Johnston. 1961. Flowering plants and ferns of the Texas Coastal Bend counties. Welder Series B-1. Sinton, Texas.

Mobberly, D. G. 1956. Taxonomy and distribution of the genus *Spartina*. Iowa State College Jour. Sci. 30(4):471-574.

Nicora, E. G. 1962. Revalidacion del genero de gramineas *Neeragrostis* de la flora Norteamericana. Revi. Argent. de Agron. 29:1-11.

Norquest, Clinton E. 1941. Climate of Texas in *Climate* and *Man*. U. S. Dept. Agr. Yearbook pp. 1129-1146.

Oakes, Harvey, Curtis Godfrey and Jack Barton. 1958. Land resource areas of Texas. Tex. Agr. Ext. Svc. L-400. 4 pp.

Pilger, R. 1954. Das system der Gramineae unter Ausschluss den Bambusiodeae. Bot. Jahrb. 76:281-384.

Prat, H. 1936. La systematique des Graminees. Ann. Soc. Nat. Bot. Ser. 24:165-258.

Raven, P. H. 1960. The correct name for rescuegrass. Brittonia 12:219-221.

Rominger, J. M. 1962. Taxonomy of *Setaria* (Gramineae) in North America. Illinois Biol. Monograph. No. 29. The Univ. of Ill. Press, Urbana.

Rowell, C. M., Jr. 1957. A provisional check list of the flora of the Rob & Bessie Welder Wildlife Foundation Refuge, San Patricio County, Texas, 14 pp. mimeo.

Small, J. K. 1903. Flora of the southeastern United States. 1392 pp. New York (published by the author).

Stebbins, G. L. 1956. Cytogenetics and evolution of the grass family. Amer. Jour. Bot. 43:890-905.

————, and B. Crampton. 1961. A suggested revision of the grass genera of temperate North America. Recent Advances in Botany, The Natural Classification of the Gramineae 133-145. Univ. of Toronto Press.

Swallen, J. R. 1963. New species of *Digitaria* and *Trichachne*. Rhodora 65:355-357.

Tateoka, T. 1957. Miscellaneous papers on the phylogeny of the Poaceae (10). Proposition of a new phylogenetic system of Poaceae. Jour. Japanese Bot. 32: 275-287.

————. 1961. A biosystematic study of *Tridens*. Amer. Jour. Bot. 48: 565-573.

Thronthwaite, C. W. 1948. An approach towards a rational classification of climate. Geogr. Rev. 38: 55-94.

Van Tieghem, P. 1897. Morphologie de l'embryon et de la plantule chez les Graminees et les Cyperacees. Ann. Sci. Nat. Bot. VIII, 3: 359-309.

INDEX TO COMMON NAMES

Common Name	Page
A	
African jointtail	98
Alkali sacaton	156
Angleton bluestem	16
Annual bluegrass	138
Arizona cottontop	59
Australian bluestem	17
B	
Bahiagrass	130
Balsamscale	71
Barley	84
Barnyardgrass	65
Basketgrass	101
Bearded sprangletop	90
Bentgrass	13
Bermudagrass	58
Big bluestem	16
Big sandbur	46
Bitter panicum	105
Bluegrass	138
Blue panicum	107
Bluestem	15
Bristle basketgrass	101
Bristlegrass	139
Broadleaf signalgrass	38
Broadleaf uniola	178
Brome	38
Broomsedge bluestem	17
Brownseed paspalum	130
Browntop panicum	109
Buffalograss	42
Buffelgrass	42
Bunch cutgrass	84
Burgrass	162
Buryseed chloris	47
Bushy bluestem	16
C	
Canada wildrye	71
Canarygrass	135
Cane bluestem	16
Carolina canarygrass	135
Carolina foxtail	13
Carolina jointtail	98
Carpetgrass	33
Clubhead cutgrass	84
Coastal Bermuda	58
Coast cockspur	65
Coast sandbur	46
Common Bermuda	58
Common carpetgrass	33
Common oat	33

Common Name	Page
Common reed	138
Cordgrass	151
Crinkleawn	162
Cupgrass	79
Curlymesquite	83
Curly threeawn	27
Cutgrass	84
D	
Dallisgrass	125
Darnel	97
Desert lovegrass	73
Dominican sprangletop	90
Dropseed	155
Dune crabgrass	59
Durban crowfootgrass	58
E	
Eastern gamagrass	175
Egyptian panicum	112
F	
Fall panicum	109
Fall witchgrass	95
Fescue	81
Filly panicum	109
Florida paspalum	125
Fourflower trichloris	162
Foxtail	13
Foxtail millet	143
Fringed chloris	49
Fringed signalgrass	38
G	
Gaping panicum	112
Giant reed	31
Goosegrass	69
Grama	33
Green sprangletop	90
Guinea grass	115
Gulf cockspur	65
Gulf cordgrass	151
Gulfdune paspalum	130
Gummy lovegrass	74
H	
Hairyawn muhly	101
Hairy crabgrass	61
Hairy grama	36
Hairyseed paspalum	130
Halls panicum	112
Hare barley	84
Hartweg paspalum	125
Hooded windmillgrass	49
Hybrid bluestem	16

Common Name	Page
I	
Indiangrass	148
Italian rye	97
J	
Jointtail	97
Johnsongrass	148
Junglerice	65
K	
King Ranch bluestem	17
Kleberg bluestem	16
Knotgrass	125
Knotroot bristlegrass	143
L	
Lacegrass	74
Little barley	84
Little bluestem	17
Longspike silver bluestem	17
Longspike tridens	173
Longtom	130
Louisiana cupgrass	79
Lovegrass	72
Lovegrass tridens	168
M	
Manyspiked chloris	49
Marsh millet	182
Marshhay cordgrass	151
Mat paspalum	130
Meadow dropseed	156
Mediterranean lovegrass	73
Mexican sprangletop	90
Mourning lovegrass	75
Muhly	99
N	
Nash windmillgrass	49
Nealley sprangletop	90
Nimblewill	101
O	
Oat	33
Onespike paspalum	133
Ozarkgrass	95
P	
Padre Island dropseed	160
Pampasgrass	56
Pan American balsamscale	71
Pappusgrass	123
Perennial rye	97
Pimple panicum	107
Pineywoods dropseed	156
Pink pappusgrass	124

Common Name	Page
Pink tridens	168
Plains bristlegrass	143
Prairie cupgrass	79
Prairie threeawn	31
Prairie trisetum	175
Prairie wedgescale	151
Purple dropseed	159
Purple lovegrass	78
Purple sandgrass	175
Purple threeawn	31
Purpletop	168
R	
Rabbitfoot grass	138
Rattail smutgrass	156
Red grama	38
Red lovegrass	76
Red sprangletop	90
Red threeawn	31
Redtop panicum	105
Rescuegrass	42
Rhodesgrass	49
Rice	101
Roemer threeawn	31
Roundseed panicum	119
Roundseed paspalum	125
Rustyseed paspalum	125
Ryegrass	95
S	
Saltgrass	65
Sandbur	42
Sand dropseed	157
Sandhill grass	38
Sand witchgrass	95
Sarita panicum	117
Seacoast bluestem	17
Sea oats	178
Seashore dropseed	161
Seashore paspalum	134
Seashore saltgrass	65
Shaggy crabgrass	59
Sheep panicum	119
Shoredune panicum	105
Shoregrass	99
Shortspike windmillgrass	49
Showy chloris	55
Sicklegrass	124
Sideoats grama	36
Signalgrass	38
Silky bluestem	17
Silver bluestem	17
Silveusgrass	162
Silveus lovegrass	77
Sixweeks fescue	178

Common Name	Page
Sixweeks grama	33
Slender grama	36
Slim tridens	173
Slimspike windmillgrass	47
Smooth cordgrass	151
Sourgrass	59
Southern sandbur	42
Southern witchgrass	107
Southern bristlegrass	148
Splitbeard bluestem	17
Sprangletop	89
Sprawling panicum	119
Stalked burgrass	162
St. Augustine grass	162
Stiffgrass	139
Stiffleaf chloris	49
Stinkgrass	76
Swallen lovegrass	78
Switchgrass	119

T

Common Name	Page
Tall fescue	81
Talquezal	134
Tanglehead	81
Texas bristlegrass	148
Texas brome	40
Texas cottontop	59
Texas crabgrass	61
Texas cupgrass	80
Texas grama	36
Texasgrass	178
Texas panicum	119
Texas tridens	173
Texas willkommia	178
Texas windmillgrass	49
Texas wintergrass	162
Thin paspalum	132
Threeawn	26
Tumblegrass	139
Tumble lovegrass	77
Tumble windmillgrass	55

V

Common Name	Page
Vaseygrass	133
Vine mesquite	117
Virginia wildrye	71

W

Common Name	Page
Water panicum	119
Wedgescale	151
Wheat	175
Whiplash pappusgrass	124
Whitegrass	84
White tridens	168
Whorled dropseed	159
Wild oat	33
Wildrye	70
Windmillgrass	46
Winter bentgrass	13
Witchgrass	95
Wooly panicum	115

Y

Common Name	Page
Yellow bristlegrass	143
Yellow indiangrass	148